*FAMILY
PLANNING
IN AN
EXPLODING
POPULATION*

FAMILY PLANNING IN AN EXPLODING POPULATION

by John A. O'Brien

Hawthorn Books, Inc.—Publishers—New York
W. Clement Stone, President

First Edition: 1968

Second Printing: 1968

ACKNOWLEDGMENTS

I acknowledge with gratitude the help of many minds and hands in the preparation of this volume. I am indebted especially to our scholarly contributors and to various publications for the following permissions:

"The World's Soaring Population" ("Population Explosion Demands Worldwide Action"), reprinted by permission from the January 8, 1964, issue of *The Christian Century*. Copyright 1964 Christian Century Foundation.

"The Problem of People," reprinted by permission from the Autumn 1965 issue of *Harvard Today*, Cambridge, Massachusetts.

"Headed for Disaster," reprinted by permission from "Poverty of Abundance," Planned Parenthood–World Population, New York.

"The Facts of Life," reprinted by permission from the August 10, 1966, issue of *The Christian Century*. Copyright 1966 Christian Century Foundation.

"Responsible Parenthood" ("Family Planning in an Exploding Population"), reprinted by permission from the August 28, 1963, issue of *The Christian Century*. Copyright 1963 Christian Century Foundation.

"Birth Control: The Only Answer" ("The Need for Information on Fertility Control"), paper presented at the First Annual Program on Fertility Control, State University of New York at Buffalo, November 12–13, 1965, reprinted with permission.

"Our Experience with Rhythm," reprinted by permission from *Population Crisis*, Part 2, U. S. Government Printing Office, Washington, D. C., 1966.

"Family Planning," reprinted by permission from the October 1967 issue of *Missouri Medicine*, the journal of the Missouri State Medical Association.

To
President Lyndon B. Johnson
John D. Rockefeller III
Senator Ernest F. Gruening
For their dedicated leadership in the
struggle to solve the problem
of the world's soaring population
before calamity befalls the human race
this Book is dedicated

CONTENTS

Next to the pursuit of peace, the really great challenge to the human family is the race between food supply and population increase. That race today is being lost.

—President Lyndon B. Johnson

PREFACE

The pioneers of earlier centuries hewed their way across a continent, sailed out on uncharted seas, and braved climatic conditions with little protection. They explored new lands, sometimes bringing disease, sometimes dying of a malady unknown to them.

Today's pioneers are different.

They are hurtling into outer space to explore that unknown area. They are perfecting cures for dread diseases which killed so many of their forebears. They live daily lives which include the modern, labor-saving devices about which their ancestors only dreamed. Their days are enhanced by inventions which give them time to read and paint and write, to learn more about history, to prepare for the twenty-first century.

But for two thirds of the world's inhabitants life is at best barely tolerable and little changed from past ages. Families are hungry, illiterate, ill-housed, poorly clothed. For these people, including some who live in our own United States, life offers no more than day-to-day existence. No greater challenge confronts us than the need to find the way to improve the quality of life on earth, to make certain that each child is a wanted child, one who can be loved and adequately clothed, fed, and educated.

If we are to solve the population problems of our own country and help others overseas who wish not merely to make quality a part of daily living but to obviate mass starvation and chaos, we must let those concerned know that birth control means acceptable to all are available now.

Certainly coercion should never be used. What is sought is that all people should have access to this information about contraception and, thereafter, freedom of choice both as to whether they wish to receive information on the subject or not, and, having received it, whether they wish to utilize it by any of the various methods available.

This should be entirely within the realm of the individual's freedom of choice. All efforts to impose either one method of birth control or another, or not to use any such method, should be left wholly to the individual and should be in keeping with his or her own individual beliefs and conscience.

Perhaps no one reform in our time—the making of this knowledge available—will be more conducive to human happiness, will obviate more personal tragedies, will do more to preserve the family, the most essential unit of human society. The knowledge of how to limit, space, and control births will indeed spell a new birth of freedom for mankind. Because this book presents that great truth with convincing cogency, it renders a great service to men and women everywhere.

ERNEST GRUENING
United States Senator
from Alaska

EDITOR'S FOREWORD

The purpose of this work is to show that the world is facing a crisis which threatens the very existence of the human race and to indicate the measures that must be taken to stave off the greatest disaster in human history. The crisis results from the unprecedented population explosion throughout the world, especially in the underdeveloped countries least capable of sustaining it.

As the subject involves many disciplines, I have enlisted the assistance of top-rank specialists in all the relevant fields: demography, economics, anthropology, chemistry, finance, engineering, sociology, government, political science, ethics, and theology. This renders possible an all-around expertise, which no single scholar could command.

In any realistic study of the population problem, the position of the Catholic Church must be considered. Its teachings concern not only its own members but also the general public, for its views on the policy of branches of the government—municipal, state, and federal —on birth control affect legislation on all these levels. Hence we have not shied away from this delicate but important phase of a pluralistic society's effort to regulate its growth by methods in accordance with the different ethical and religious convictions of its citizens.

Pope John XXIII, President Kennedy, and Vatican Council II brought to the Church a new openness which encourages all its members, especially the laity, to speak out on issues on which they have some competence and thus help to establish public opinion within the Church. Consequently readers will be pleasantly surprised at the new candor and openness with which Catholic scholars have expressed themselves on the role of the government in family planning.

I have been deeply involved with the problem of birth control for more than thirty years. During the Great Depression in the early '30s, I was greatly concerned with the plight of Catholic families. With millions unemployed and on public relief, Catholic wives were greatly worried over the prospect of a new pregnancy when they were unable to care for the children they already had. They stood in desperate need of help. "Live as brother and sister" in continual continence was not the answer to their problem.

Fortunately at this time the findings of two gynecologists, Dr. Kyusaku Ogino of Japan and Dr. Hermann Knaus of Austria, each working independently concerning the rhythm of periods of sterility and fertility in the menstrual cycle, became known. Their data supplied the basis for the law of rhythm with the prospect of determining with reasonable accuracy the so-called "safe" period. This would be a godsend to millions of women and especially Catholics, who wanted desperately to postpone pregnancy without living as celibates.

I wrote to Dr. Knaus and secured his research findings. With the help of several gynecologists I explained the significance of these findings in a lengthy article covering several pages in *Our Sunday Visitor,* the most widely circulated Catholic weekly magazine in the United States of America, in the issue of November 26, 1933. This was the first article on the subject in a magazine of national circulation in the United States and it brought a deluge of mail.

From all parts of the country streamed in letters from anxious parents, pastors, and even physicians, asking for still more information about this newly discovered method of regulating conception. Accordingly I prepared a seventy-two-page booklet, *Legitimate Birth Control,* presenting additional information, and had it carefully checked by Dr. Henry Schmitz, head of the gynecology department of Loyola University Medical School in Chicago.

It was published in 1934 and carried an Introduction by Most Rev. John F. Noll, editor of *Our Sunday Visitor* and bishop of Fort Wayne. In it he said: "I believe this brochure by Father O'Brien is the best ever written on the subject of birth control." Published as a public service, and sold at actual cost (15¢), the booklet brought some assistance to thousands of families in the throes of the worst depression in our history.

In the following years additional light was thrown upon the rhythm method by medical research, disclosing factors which tend to alter the regularity of the menstrual cycle. Accordingly with the assistance of Dr. Hermann Knaus, Dr. Raoul De Guchteneere of the Lambert Foundation, Brussels, Belgium, and Dr. Henry Schmitz—three eminent gynecologists—I wrote a 160-page book, *Natural Birth Control,* published in 1938. This provided additional guidance in the practice of the rhythm method.

For several years, however, some of the officials in the Church, especially in Rome, were becoming increasingly concerned over the number of Catholic women practicing rhythm. The worst of the Depression had now passed, and there was the feeling in certain quarters that rhythm was not conducive to the begetting of the large families, which have so long been extolled as the Catholic ideal.

Under instructions from a member of the Roman Curia, the apostolic delegate sent a directive to the Catholic bishops of the United States to discourage the spread of information about rhythm among Catholic families. A directive to this effect was then sent by each bishop to his pastors. This was followed by the requirement that couples were to secure permission from their pastoral counselor or confessor to practice rhythm.

This meant they had to present sufficient reasons, such as the health of the mother or the finances of the family, to justify their regulation of births. This was the situation which obtained virtually till Vatican Council II. While requesting Catholic parents to keep in mind procreation as one of the primary ends of marriage, the Council decreed that it was up to parents themselves to apply the principles formulated by the Church to their marriage and for them alone to determine the number of offspring they could best provide for.

I was disturbed over what seemed to me to be the tendency of Catholics in not a few communities to impose, perhaps unconsciously, the implications of their belief concerning the evil of contraception upon the general public. This stems from the Catholic concept of the natural law as forbidding contraception and as binding all people. This in spite of the fact that most Protestant churches have approved contraception not only as morally permissible but even as obligatory in many, if not most, cases.

Accordingly I wrote an article, "Let's Take Birth Control Out of Politics," for *Look* magazine, October 6, 1961, in which I stressed the all-important truth that in a pluralistic society no one religious organization has the right, through political pressure or legislative enactment, to impose its distinctive creedal or moral code or its practical implications upon those of other faiths. I developed this thesis again in a series of three articles published simultaneously in *The Christian Century* and *Ave Maria* magazines, and in CBS and NBC television programs over nationwide networks reaching many millions.

The deluge of ensuing mail from the articles and TV programs provided me with an authentic insight into the minds of the people of this country afforded few individuals in America. This has been supplemented by attending innumerable conferences of top-ranking scholars and scientists on birth control and the population problem, as well as by participating in many colloquia on these twin subjects at leading universities.

It is this experience of more than thirty years of dealing with virtually every phase of the twin problems of birth control and population explosion upon which I have drawn in editing this book. It is the hope of my scholarly contributors and of myself that this work will help to remove birth control from further controversy and unite all the people of this nation and of the world in the urgent and imperative task of launching constructive measures to control the world's population, increasing with frightening speed, before civilization and human life, as we know it, are doomed.

In editing the chapters by the various contributors, I have not undertaken to make their projections of the population growth of the various nations square with one another. There is a legitimate diversity of opinion here, and even the most conservative estimates for the decades ahead carry the threat of disaster unless action is taken promptly.

For the statistics in my chapters I am indebted to Professor Philip M. Hauser, Director of the Population Research and Training Center, University of Chicago, and former U.S. Representative to the United Nations Population Commission.

Incidentally, the views expressed in my chapters reflect my own personal thinking on the highly controversial subject of family planning, and I assume full responsibility for any statement that may be open to possible misunderstanding.

J.A.O.

Part I
THE POPULATION
EXPLOSION

1

THE WORLD'S
SOARING POPULATION

by John A. O'Brien

Research professor of theology at the University of Notre
Dame, Dr. O'Brien has written extensively on birth control and the population problem, and has lectured on
these subjects at many of our leading universities.

According to the best historical and archaeological evidence, about
eight hundred thousand to a million years were required for the human
race to reach the 250 million mark by the beginning of the Christian
era. From that date, due to pestilence, famine, and war, the population
increased but a tiny fraction of 1 per cent per year, so that more than
sixteen centuries were required to double its size and reach 500 million. In the next 250 years, however, the world population shot up
to the one billion mark around 1850.

Then in a little more than a century, the population skyrocketed
to its present three billion mark. In the next thirty-three years—a mere
twinkling of an eye—it will more than double, according to the United
Nations demographers, reaching 6.9 billion by the year 2000. In about

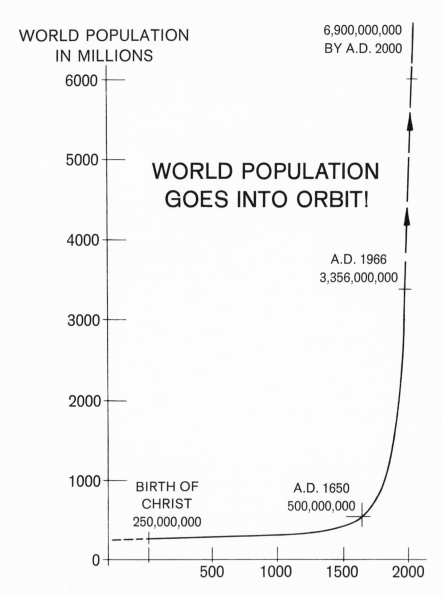

This chart is based on statistics from the Demographic Yearbook issued by the United Nations Statistical Office and Department of Economic and Social Affairs

half a lifetime the population increase will exceed the total achieved in almost a million years!

This means that about three births occur every second and about two million every week. Thus the world adds each year a population about the equivalent of Great Britain or France. With the present increase of approximately 2 per cent per year, the population will total fifty billion in less than a century and a half. Indeed if the current rate of growth should continue for 650 years, every inhabitant would have but one square foot of land surface to stand on!

The Rockefeller Foundation has devoted much of its funds to research on the population problem. Surveying the results of that extensive research, one of its top officials recently remarked, "The world has cancer and that cancer cell is man."

Egypt's Gamal Abdel Nasser declared that the world's exploding population is just as serious as the danger of nuclear war. "The growth of world population during the next twenty-five years," warns the United Nations Demographic Commission, "is at the very heart of the problem of our existence."

The skyrocketing of world population is then an utterly new phenomenon, without precedent in history. It may fairly be called a "population explosion" not for scare propaganda but in an honest effort to portray its grim and awesome reality. A calm consideration of its bearing on the life and welfare of the race is not calculated to lull one to sleep but to spur one to action.

What increases enormously the acuteness of the problem is the fact that the greatest increases in population are occurring in the underdeveloped countries least able to sustain them. In India, Pakistan, China, Africa, and Latin America, where poverty is rampant, the population has soared to new heights.

In India, where the people barely survive on an average daily diet of 1700 calories—only two-thirds of subsistence level—the yearly growth is equal to the population of Texas. Uncounted thousands spend their whole lives in the streets, owning not a foot of ground—abject beggars from birth to death.

Few Americans can visualize the accumulated anguish, torment, and degradation that lie behind such poverty. Families with from five to ten children in these underdeveloped countries live in a miserable hut of one or two rooms with a dirt floor. Riddled with disease, gnaw-ed by hunger, devoid of hope, they eke out a miserable existence rarely free from pain. Their entire life is a struggle simply to stay alive.

"We never really knew," remarked Mrs. John Kubish, wife of an American AID official, "how many millions of people constantly suffer the pangs of hunger until we went to India and Ceylon. So under-nourished are many of the people that they resemble walking skeletons.

"While in Ceylon we visited a school for the blind and deaf con-ducted by Belgian sisters near Colombo. Imagine our surprise and horror when the sister superior told us that in every case the blindness of the child was due to semistarvation. Misery, sickness, and disease from undernourishment stalk the visitor everywhere."

Such is a picture of the living conditions of millions of families in the underdeveloped countries. In the last forty years the population of Latin America doubled and is expected to reach the staggering total of 650 million by the year 2000. The annual per capita income averages but $289, and the ratio of increased income against popula-tion growth is among the worst in the world—worse even than Africa. The annual increase of approximately 3 per cent in the population more than nullifies the mere 1 per cent increase of the economy.

From behind the mass of population statistics emerge a few simple but grim human facts: One half of the world's population suffers from outright hunger. Two thirds suffers from undernourishment. Each day 150,000 people are added to the world's population and each year the total is increased by fifty million!

How are we to meet this ever-increasing threat to the health, wel-fare, and even the very existence of the race? The earth, reply not a few religious leaders, is the common patrimony of the human race and all should have access to it and its resources. Children of the same heavenly Father and members of the same human family, we are all brothers. Hence nations with abundant resources should help the underprivileged, sharing with them scientific knowledge and tech-nical skills and thus enable them to achieve a thriving economy of their own.

These are noble ideals and, if they could be achieved, their reali-zation would help mightily in closing the gap between the "have" and the "have-not" nations. It would enable the peoples of the underdeveloped countries to achieve their "revolution of mounting expectations" without violence and without surrendering their aspirations for freedom and a democratic form of government. In short, the implementation of these ideals would promote stability of governments, halt the spread of Communism, and safeguard the peace of the world.

But can these ideals be realized and, if so, how? What are the practical measures by which these goals can be reached? The answers must come chiefly from demographers, who furnish the scientific data so necessary for the formulation of sound policy on both the national and international planes.

To secure those answers we contacted, with the help of Notre Dame demographer Donald N. Barrett, twenty-five top-flight demographers, asking them to list in the order of importance and effectiveness the following measures: 1. increasing sources and supply of food for underdeveloped countries; 2. increasing their industrialization; 3. migration from heavily populated to less populated areas; 4. regulation of conception and births; 5. to suggest any other measures. We also requested them to indicate the combination of measures which they considered most important and urgent in meeting the plight of the underdeveloped nations.

The survey resulted in findings, we think, of far-reaching significance not only to demographers but also to the general public. Virtually all were agreed upon the following: 1. None of the proposed measures, or any other, can prove effective by itself. 2. What is needed is an integrated, many-faceted program which ministers simultaneously to all the basic needs of people in the underdeveloped countries to correct the imbalance between population and resources. 3. Without some regulation of conception and births, all other measures are doomed to failure.

Typical of the reasoning embodied in virtually all the replies is that of Dr. Frank W. Notestein, president of The Population Council and former director of Population Research at Princeton University. Here it is in condensed form: For a decent life it is necessary that populations be in vigorous health, educated, and relieved from crushing poverty. In most of the countries, and especially in the heavily populated ones, there is no hope for the sustained achievement of these objectives without modernization. The transition from self-sufficient peasant societies to modernized society must be made on all fronts. Agricultural development cannot go alone.

Such a transition is inordinately expensive because it involves heavy investment in health, education, and productive equipment. This investment may prove impossible unless in the course of the next few decades the rate of population growth can be brought to reasonably low levels, preferably less than 1 per cent. The current rates in the underdeveloped countries vary from 2 to 3½ per cent and present major threats to the success of a transition without widespread human catastrophe. It is this which convinces one that a reduction in the birth rate must be achieved as early as possible.

Agreeing with Dr. Notestein's reasoning, William Vogt stresses the need for developing in parents of a higher sense of responsibility for the welfare of their children and, in countries such as India and Pakistan, a postponement of marriage. He points out that, though every two decades we add to the world's population as many people as accumulated between 4000 B.C. and A.D. 1830, we have failed to develop for the population upsurge in the underdeveloped countries the necessary variety and combination of technologies. Especially interesting is his comment on the proposed shift of populations from heavily populated areas to less dense ones.

"Migration I consider something of a red herring," he says, "since faith in it tends to divert attention away from other and effective measures. Nowhere in the world will immigrants be acceptable in sufficient numbers to make a significant contribution toward solving the population problem. And internal migrations in most of the world are from the less populated to the more populated areas." With this conclusion demographers are in general agreement.

Thus Dr. Robert C. Cook, president of the Population Reference Bureau in Washington, D.C., writes: "The view quite widely held that this crisis can be ameliorated by migration, by industrialization, or by other similar means is illusionary." Demographer Arthur A. Campbell, director of the Scripps Foundation for Research in Population Problems develops this point at length.

What is the one measure which all these top-ranking demographers stress as of crucial and decisive importance in dealing with the problem precipitated by the spectacular and unprecedented skyrocketing of population? It is the regulation of conception and birth. Until we come to honest grips with this factor, we are but playing with shadows and shall never solve the problem.

Dr. Cook thus sums up admirably the conviction of all demographers: "Regulation of conception and birth to bring a balance with modern low mortality is essential in even a rather short run on a planet of finite size and resources. Indefinite multiplication of people cannot long continue and would in the end be disastrous. Such control cannot come quickly. At the very best, a lag of a generation must be expected even under the most favorable circumstances."

Such, too, is the conclusion reached by the Catholic Institute for Social Research in Geneva, Switzerland, as expressed in a lengthy statement by its director, the noted demographer G. H. L. Zeegers. Dr. Cook considers that statement the "most effective" exposition of the interplay of all the factors essential for the solution of the population problem that he has seen.

"Regulation of family size," stresses Philip M. Hauser, director of Population Research at Chicago University, "is becoming increasingly imperative. Other means are at best only temporary palliatives. Dealing with them is but a delaying action." Writing in the *Catholic Mind,* the British scholar S. Z. Young discusses such palliatives as improvement in food distribution, more intensive and scientific agriculture, drawing on resources of the sea, and development of underpopulated areas.

He then frankly acknowledges that these measures "are irrelevant to the population policies of the underdeveloped countries today. Their problem is that their population is increasing faster than food and other basic production . . . . What many underdeveloped countries are seeking, notably India and Pakistan, is a brake on population, which will bring its rate of increase below that of essential production and thus make possible industrial development and improvement of the pitiful low living standards of their people."

The failure to deal with this crucial aspect of the problem wipes out most of the benefits of our foreign aid. The United States has shipped millions of tons of food to the underdeveloped nations. At the end of World War II, the United States launched the Marshall Plan, which gave a total of $15 billion to seventeen nations. But our foreign aid now goes to ninety-seven countries and five territories!

Our foreign aid program has now reached an annual cost of approximately $10 billion, including interest on money borrowed to finance it. At the end of the year 1966, the cost of foreign aid in the postwar period since July 1, 1945, exceeded the staggering total of $150 billion.

With what results? It increased the income of the underdeveloped countries by 3 per cent a year during the '50s, but two thirds of this was immediately wiped out because of the 200 million new mouths to feed. The result: a microscopic gain of but $1.00 per person per year! It is almost like pouring money into quicksand.

Because of the introduction of antibiotics and other "miracle" drugs and insecticides in massive public health programs, half or two thirds of the infants and children who would otherwise have died are now kept alive. The result is that more than half of the world's population is now under twenty years of age—all demanding food, clothing, housing, and an education. The life span is also greatly lengthened. As a consequence of these two factors the population has soared into orbit, throwing the economy into a tailspin in spite of all the billions of American dollars poured into it each year. Such is the vicious circle, the trap, in which both the underdeveloped peoples and our aid program are caught.

"Population growth," warns Eugene R. Black, former president of the World Bank, "threatens to nullify all our efforts to raise living standards in many of the poorer countries." Lord Casey, Australia's veteran Foreign Minister, says: "The very large amount of development money . . . is being largely wasted." The French sociologist Germaine Tillion says with even greater bluntness: "A catastrophe is becoming imminent in those countries." Thought to be forever vanished, the grim ghost of the melancholy Malthus is coming back on the scene.

The failure to help the underdeveloped countries solve their population problems not only largely nullifies our foreign aid program but renders more distant the day when these people will be able to stand on their own financial feet—the goal of every self-respecting people. It also raises the question as to how much longer our own economy can stand the strain of pouring out billions of the taxpayers' money, when millions of our own people are unemployed and the burden of defense armament mounts steeply and steadily. "Something," as the saying goes, "will have to give."

Testifying before the Senate Agricultural Committee, Secretary of Agriculture Orville Freeman declared that the United States "cannot by itself do the gigantic long-term job of feeding an exploding population in all the food deficit areas of the world."

Secretary Freeman pointed out that the world's population, now 3.5 billion, will increase by one billion in the next fifteen years and that "four fifths of the increase will occur in parts of the world where the fertility of the people has outstripped the fertility of the soil." He stated that millions of people in the underdeveloped nations die because malnutrition has sapped their resistance to childhood diseases, and millions who survive are permanently handicapped, physically or mentally.

Mass starvation was prevented in India in 1966 by emergency wheat shipments from the United States. These were increased to the limit of port and internal distribution facilities and totalled approximately ten million tons by the end of the year. In spite of such shipments of unprecedented magnitude there were local shortages and riots in some cities. If present trends continue, India's rampaging population, now 500 million, will reach the 695 million mark by 1980.

This means that in the brief span of fourteen years it will increase by as much as the present population of the entire United States. Experts of the United States Department of Agriculture, of the United Nations Food and Agricultural Organization, and demographers at the Population Research centers of our universities are in unanimous agreement that the present trends will produce an acute world food deficit.

Unless immediate and world-wide efforts are made to reverse these trends, we are facing the frightening prospect of mass starvation, riots, and revolutions. In short, it is physically impossible for the United States, with but 6 per cent of the world's population and 7 per cent of its land surface, to provide food for the billions of people in the underdeveloped countries whose population is soaring at rates of speed unprecedented in all of human history.

After exhaustive investigation of this situation Chesly Manly of the Chicago *Tribune* reached the following sobering conclusions: "The four horsemen of the Apocalypse—war, famine, pestilence, and death—will take their toll of millions in Asia, Africa, and Latin America." That prediction will be fulfilled unless the whole civilized world awakens to the threat facing it today.

There is no need, however, to press the panic button. But neither should we ignore a problem that yearly becomes more serious. Second only to the danger of nuclear war is the threat of overpopulation—a form of cancer on a world scale. Not alarmists but sober scientists after years of dispassionate study sound this warning.

The gravity of the world population explosion was spelled out in vivid detail by Dr. John L. Battenfield, in an address to a Catholic congress in New York on September 3, 1962. Pointing out that the current annual increase of 1.7 per cent in the world population is 850 times greater than the rhythm of expansion prior to the year 1600, he pleaded for wholehearted Catholic support of an international aid program, to assist the underdeveloped countries to deal effectively with the problem of their soaring populations.

Worth heeding is the testimony of two eminent scientists. "The world's population," says Vannevar Bush, former president of Carnegie Institution at Washington, "is increasing at a rate which renders distress, famine, and disintegration inevitable unless we hold our numbers within reason. Man is headed for catastrophe unless he mends his ways and takes thought for the morrow."

Demographer Harrison Brown of the California Institute of Technology agrees: "Rapid population growth works against practically all the long-range goals which men and women the world over share. Global family planning is an essential factor in any sensible program for resource development. Of all the problems which confront our unhappy world it is by all odds the most urgent and the most critical. Yet, ironically, it is the problem which is receiving the least attention."

The soaring population of the world was the subject discussed at five population conferences at the University of Notre Dame which brought together top-ranking scientists in demography, sociology, gynecology, anthropology, economics, and moral theology. Experts came not only from the leading institutions of learning in this country but also from foreign lands. They represented all religious faiths.

They all arrived at the conclusion that the rapid rate at which the world's population is growing cannot long continue without great danger to cultural and moral values and to the normal life of the human race. Reflecting this universal conviction, Dr. George N. Shuster, director of the population conference, said: "All demographers, whether they be Catholic or not, are agreed that mankind must henceforth limit its power to procreate. Even if we assume that the world's food supply can be vastly increased and that economic productivity will reach hitherto undreamed of levels, simple arithmetic plainly points to inevitable disaster if the growth rate from two billion to six billion in eighty years were to be maintained."

The growing world-wide consciousness of the gravity and urgency of the world population problem found articulation at Vatican Council II, which brought together bishops from all parts of the world. In its constitution on *The Church in the Modern World,* the Council acknowledges that at times conditions will require couples to limit their offspring. "Serious disturbances," declares the constitution, "are caused in families by modern economic conditions, by influences at once social and psychological, and by the demands of civil society. Finally, in certain parts of the world, problems resulting from population growth are generating concern. . . . This Council realizes that [such] modern conditions often keep couples from arranging their married lives harmoniously, and that they find themselves in circumstances where at least temporarily the size of their families should not be increased."

In the light of the unprecedented soaring of the population, Father John C. Ford, S.J., and Father Gerald Kelly, S.J., state: "It may well be that population pressures in a given region may constitute a legitimate excusing cause from the affirmative obligation [to have children], and that at some future date population pressures could conceivably reach the point where they would create strict duties not to procreate."

The crowning piece of evidence of both the reality and urgence of the population problem is *A Statement of Conviction,* signed by thirty-nine Nobel prize winners and presented to the secretary-general of the United Nations on November 17, 1960. After describing the present unprecedented rate of population growth and the projection of a population of about seven billion by the year 2000, as estimated by the United Nations demographers, they say:

"In spite of technological advances the earth cannot provide much longer enough food and minerals for a population which is increasing more than geometrically; unless a favorable balance of population and resources is achieved with a minimum of delay, there is in prospect a Dark Age of human misery, famine, under-education and unrest which could generate growing panic, exploding into wars fought to appropriate the dwindling means of survival."

The conclusion of these scientists and scholars from many countries was confirmed by the National Academy of Sciences, the largest body of scientists in the United States. After lengthy study of the population problem, the academy reached the following significant conclusions:

"1. Nearly all our economic, social and political problems become more difficult to solve in the face of uncontrolled population growth.

"2. It commands the attention of every nation and society; the problem is no less grave for the technically advanced nations than for the less developed.

"3. The population problem can be successfully attacked by developing new methods of fertility regulation and by implementing programs of family planning widely and rapidly throughout the world.

"4. The over-all task is to achieve universal acceptance of the desirability of planning and controlling family size."

It is high time not only for our nation but for all nations to hearken to the warning of the scholars and scientists of the world upon the urgent necessity of launching measures to regulate the world's soaring population or to face disaster.

2

THE PROBLEM OF PEOPLE

by Roger Revelle

Dr. Revelle is the Richard Saltonstall Professor of Population Policy in the School of Public Health and director of the University-wide Center for Population Studies at Harvard University.

Present rates of human population growth confront us with a problem that is unique in the long history of our species. Hundreds of thousands of years were required to produce, by A.D. 1850, a living population of one billion people. The second billion took seventy-five years more, from 1850 to 1925, but only another thirty-five years until 1960 were needed for the third billion. The fourth billion will be here by 1980, and the fifth ten years later, by 1990. Unless drastic changes in birth or death rates occur, the population increase between now and the year 2000 will be larger than the entire present population of the earth.

Bringing down rates of population growth to a manageably low level will require far more knowledge and experience than we now possess. Economic, sociological, medical, and educational research on a large scale and a wide front are urgently required. The problem may well be the most difficult mankind has ever faced, for its solution lies in controlling one of the basic drives of all living things—to reproduce.

When we try to bring down death rates, every human instinct is on our side. Nearly everyone wants to live longer. Everyone thinks other people should live longer. When we try to bring down birth rates, most human instincts work against us. It is not merely a question of the sex instinct; it is a question of the meaning of life—the joy of having children, the feeling that one is a complete human being only if he has children.

The number of human beings on the earth may ultimately be limited by one or more of many factors—the total energy available for food and material production, the biological and psychosomatic results of crowding, or, more hopefully, the conscious and deliberate decisions of individual men and women.

At least a temporary check on population growth could come from the increased area of cities. During the next century, most people will live in cities. The farm population of the world will not increase very much, because we are approaching the limit of the number of farmers who can be effectively employed. At present rates of increase, city populations would multiply perhaps forty times within the next hundred years. Even in the next fifty years, the Indian city of Calcutta could grow to sixty million. Calcutta today is a house of misery. What would it be like with sixty million people? Our own cities in the United States might reach sizes that we can hardly imagine.

As a city becomes bigger, the density of population within it tends to diminish; consequently the total area covered by cities in the middle of the twenty-first century could be a hundred times larger than today, and equal to perhaps one fifth of the entire land surface of the earth. The problems of supplying the wants and removing the waste of such sprawling monster cities would require wholly new levels of technology.

Although population growth clearly cannot continue indefinitely, it is equally clear that given the right social and economic conditions, and a sufficiently high technology, the resources of the earth could support a much larger number of human beings than are now alive. The real and present question is not population size in the future but the rate of increase today. How shall we provide decent conditions of life for the living generation, conditions in which men and women can live, and children can grow up, free of the desperate want experienced by the majority of human beings in this century? This is the urgent thrust of the population problem.

Present rates of population growth in India, Pakistan, and Egypt are probably between 2.5 per cent and 3 per cent per year. In Brazil and some other South American countries, annual rates are more than 3 per cent. The populations of Costa Rica and the Philippines are growing by perhaps 4 per cent per year. A 3 per cent growth rate means a doubling of population in twenty-three years; with a 4 per cent rate the doubling time is seventeen years.

These figures are typical of many of the underdeveloped countries. They underlie the fact that the world population, which increased by 1 per cent a year in 1940, is now increasing by 2 per cent. Although total national incomes are rising, the increased production must be divided among ever larger numbers of people, and standards of living remain nearly static. Men have to run faster and faster just to stay where they are.

In the two American continents today, about as many people live north of the Rio Grande as south of it. But by the year 2000, there will be twice as many people in Latin America as in the United States and Canada. In the world as a whole, unless a drastic change occurs, people who live in desperate misery and poverty will constitute the overwhelming fraction of the human population.

Compared with 1935, food production in many countries has barely kept up with population growth, and in some cases has fallen behind. Average food production per capita for Latin America is less now than it was before World War II. Were it not for food imports from the United States and other Western countries, the diets of the people of India and Pakistan would be even more deficient today than in 1935. The average person in the subcontinent is getting less food than he needs, by perhaps 20 per cent. His diet is particularly deficient in high-quality protein. Without sufficient protein of the right kind, the health of adults is worsened and their life span shortened, but, what may be even more disastrous, the mental development of children probably is retarded.

Egypt is a large country in terms of area, but nearly all of it is a lifeless desert. Only the delta and the flat flood plain of the Nile are suitable for agriculture. This arable region covers about six million acres, approximately equal to the area of Massachusetts. Today there are thirty million Egyptians, most of whom are trying to make a living on these fertile acres. This is the highest density for a rural population anywhere in the world, about three thousand people per square mile.

The population is increasing at such a rate that there will be sixty million Egyptians by the year 1988—just twenty years from now. One dreads the possibility that the population will become stabilized at some figure short of this by malnutrition and disease, that situation of "misery and vice" foreseen by Thomas Robert Malthus, the prophetic eighteenth-century demographer. The Aswan High Dam will provide about a 40 per cent increase in agricultural production, which means that unless they can halt their population increase Egyptians will be able to feed themselves at present levels only for another ten to twelve years.

In India, with a growth rate of around 2.5 per cent per year, the number of children below fifteen years of age is 45 per cent of the entire population. Nearly one person in two is a child or younger adolescent, whereas with a slowly growing population under modern conditions of life expectancy, this proportion is less than 25 per cent. The high proportion of children and adolescents to adults means that the nation cannot save for capital investment without great difficulty, because most of what the adults produce is needed for immediate consumption. Yet the ability to invest savings in order to increase the means of production is an essential requirement for economic development.

We in the United States need to examine more closely the social and economic costs of rising numbers of people in our own country. Our population is increasing at about 1.5 per cent a year, considerably less than the rate in the less developed parts of the world. Yet even this rate of growth brings many problems. Increases in per capita costs of pollution abatement, municipal water supplies, outdoor recreation, and urban transportation are all consequences of our increasing numbers. Perhaps more serious is the decline in the quality of life: the crowding and dangers in our parks; the fact that our water does not taste as good as it used to; that many of our fellow citizens waste one or two hours each day driving to and from work under what can only be described as miserable conditions. One has to ask whether juvenile delinquency, student alienation in the universities, and unemployment among untrained youth are not also partly related to our rapid population growth and, if so, how should this affect our national thought and action?

During the past two decades our rate of population growth was considerably higher than it is today. As a result, the number of high school students will increase from ten million in 1960 to fifteen million in 1970. Within these ten years we must build new high schools equal in capacity to half of all those now in use in the United States. This is a hard thing for the taxpayers to face, and in general they do not seem really willing to face it. In many communities the quality of our high school facilities is going down.

The number of college and university students is growing from about four million in 1960 to about twelve million in 1980. Everybody who has children of college age realizes how hard this is on young people. It is equally hard on the colleges. Both the necessary construction of facilities and the required increase in the numbers of able teachers seem to be almost insoluble problems.

In the first edition of his famous *An Essay on the Principles of Population,* published in 1798, Malthus reached the pessimistic conclusion that an equilibrium between human births and deaths could be established only at a relatively high death rate. That is, war, famine, and disease, or "misery and vice," as he put it, would kill people off as fast as others were born. Man's fate was to reproduce himself right up to the limit of disease and starvation, and he had no control over what would happen to him.

Some modern Neo-Malthusians, who share Malthus' early views, claim that the population of any organism will continue to increase until it reaches the edge of subsistence or of control by enemy organisms. They believe this is as true of men as it is of mice or elephants —the only difference being that with different organisms different amounts of time might be required.

History and experience show that this doctrine is bad sociology; recent biological research shows it is bad biology. Experiments with laboratory rats demonstrate that when too many of these animals are forced to live together in too small a space, their behavior patterns become radically abnormal and they effectively cease to reproduce themselves. Wild animals, particularly predators, seem to limit their own numbers in various ways. Some species do this by exercising territoriality: Each dominant male controls an area of a certain size, on which he will not allow other males of the same species to encroach, even though he may be indifferent to the presence of males of a different species.

Malthus himself changed his mind before he published the second edition of his *Essay* in 1802. In gathering data for the second edition, he observed that the population of Switzerland had remained nearly static for several generations, even though death rates had substantially declined. He concluded that birth rates must have decreased in proportion to the decline in death rates, and that this was due to the postponement of marriage by Swiss couples until they could inherit or buy enough farm land to support a family. He then added a third process, "moral restraint," to the dismal duo, "misery and vice," which he had previously believed were the only causes of population limitation. His new edition concluded with these (for Malthus) optimistic words:

". . . it is hoped that the general result of the inquiry is such as not to make us give up the improvement of human society in despair. The partial good which seems to be attainable is worthy of all our exertions; is sufficient to direct our efforts, and animate our prospects. And although we cannot expect that the virtue and happiness of mankind will keep pace with the brilliant career of physical discovery; yet, if we are not wanting ourselves, we may confidently indulge the hope that, to no unimportant extent, they will be influenced by its progress and will partake in its success."

In both ancient and medieval times, there were occasions when human beings exercised control over their own populations through the aggregate of the individual decisions of many couples.

During the last two or three centuries before the fall of the Roman Empire (A.D. 476) the population of Italy steadily declined. Despite governmental attempts, by means of penalties and rewards, to increase the population, the people just did not reproduce themselves in sufficient numbers.

In Tuscany, between A.D. 1200 and 1400, the population decreased by nearly 75 per cent. The tax rolls and other sources of vital statistics are very good for this period in Tuscany, and they show that throughout most of these two centuries the average number of children per household was two or less. We do not know what kept the people from reproducing, but a factor that may have strongly influenced them was a decline in the prices of farm products compared to interest rates on farm mortgages. This brought increasing poverty and misery to the countryside.

Throughout the nineteenth century, there was in Europe and North America a steady fall in death rates from disease, due perhaps primarily to the introduction of such public health practices as smallpox vaccination and improved sanitation. The excess of births over deaths was eventually succeeded by a decline in birth rates. As both birth rates and death rates diminished they grew closer together, so that rates of population growth, especially in certain European nations, gradually but markedly decreased during the hundred years before World War II. Demographers have called this series of events the "Demographic Transition."

Several developed nations in our own time, notably Japan, Hungary, Sweden, and Italy, have essentially stabilized their populations. For example, in Japan the birth rate is not much more than fifteen per thousand per year, while the death rate is about seven per thousand, so that the population is growing at around 0.8 per cent a year. But a moment's thought will show that an annual death rate of seven per thousand cannot continue for very long. Otherwise people would live to be 150 years old. The death rate must rise to around fifteen per thousand if the human life span is to remain at about seventy years.

Today we know something that Malthus did not: Nearly all societies attempt some population control, though the methods used may be relatively ineffective. Among the most effective of the traditional methods is abortion.

In some countries, such as Japan, Hungary, and the Soviet Union, which have legalized abortion and have introduced new, comparatively safe techniques, the number of abortions each year is believed to be about the same as the number of live births. We know less about the ratio of abortions to live births in countries where abortions are illegal. In Chile and Colombia, and perhaps in other South American nations, a high percentage of all hospital admissions in the obstetric wards is of women suffering from infections or injuries as a result of illegal abortions.

In the last few years, two very effective contraceptive methods have been introduced—the steroid pills and the intrauterine loops or coils, commonly called IUDs. IUDs can be manufactured very cheaply, since they are simply small pieces of polyethylene plastic, and they can be inserted fairly inexpensively. These devices are already being widely used in Taiwan and South Korea. The Indian Medical Council has accepted them as a safe and effective contraceptive method, and plans are now under way for nationwide programs of introducing the devices in both India and Pakistan. Although IUDs can be retained by only about four out of five women who attempt to use them— the other 20 per cent involuntarily expel them or the devices have to be removed for medical reasons—it should nevertheless be possible with their use to bring about a significant reduction in birth rates throughout the subcontinent during the next fifteen years.

One must not be too optimistic, however, concerning the resulting decline in the rate of population growth, because the death rate can be expected to fall during this time from the present seventeen to twenty-five per thousand to perhaps ten or below, which would mean that for some time to come the rate of population growth would still be more than 2 per cent, or a doubling within one generation.

In ancient Rome, medieval Tuscany, and eighteenth-century Switzerland, death rates were high, and only a slight pressure for population control was needed to tip the balance between births and deaths. In nineteenth-century Europe and North America, the early stages of the demographic transition took place in an environment of increasing prosperity and rapidly spreading literacy. The twentieth-century countries that have stabilized their populations are comparatively well developed both educationally and economically.

But none of these conditions exists today in the countries where rapid rates of population growth are a tragically serious problem. Most of their people are illiterate and nearly all are desperately poor.

Their death rates are actually or potentially lower than were death rates in any country prior to the last few decades. Consequently, population control methods must be much more effective than in the past, if population growth is to be sufficiently diminished. On the positive side, there is evidence that significant numbers of village women and their husbands strongly desire not to have more children, and are eager to use effective birth control methods that are within their physical and educational capabilities.

Although there are great differences between the problems of death control and birth control, a direct relationship exists between birth rates and death rates, particularly rates of infant and child mortality. In many countries, grown-up children who will support their aged parents are the chief form of social security. If a man and his wife do not have at least one adult male child, they have little to look forward to when they can no longer work to support themselves. Under conditions of high child mortality, the average married couple needs to produce many children to be sufficiently certain that at least one boy will survive to become a man. Only in this way can they ensure their own future security. Whenever infant and child mortality can be brought down to a low level, the probability in an individual family that a male child will survive becomes very much greater, and the pressure for large numbers of children will correspondingly lessen. This is one of the principal reasons the profession of public health needs to be deeply involved in programs of family planning and population control.

In some less developed countries, rates of population growth might be reduced by the introduction of a social security system, whereby the government helped men to be their brothers' keepers. Here we come up against a moral problem—public versus private morality. In the Western world we believe we have a responsibility toward society as a whole, toward all men and all women in our society. In many less developed countries, the individual's responsibility toward other human beings is just as intense, but it does not extend beyond the family or the blood relations.

These are problems that universities may be able to do something about. One reason for thinking so is that universities have in the past helped to solve other problems that looked somewhat like these: problems in medicine and public health, sanitation, human behavior, and social structure. Accordingly, Harvard established in 1965 a new University-wide Center for Population Studies, under the leadership of the School of Public Health.

The need to reduce rates of population growth is so urgent in many countries that immediate action on a large scale should be undertaken. Yet we in the university must try at the same time to deepen our understanding and improve our practice. We need to work in real societies with all their environmental and cultural differences, not only to discover underlying generalities, but also to learn how to adapt our actions to fit the range of human conditions.

Much of the needed understanding will come from experience gained in birth control and family planning programs; members of the university should participate in these programs if they are to learn as much as possible from them. Because of its long experience and broad involvement in field projects throughout the world, the School of Public Health is uniquely fitted to work out appropriate means of participation.

Our immediate concerns are family planning, population control, and the balancing of resources development against population growth, but the members of the center will also inevitably be interested in some long-range questions. Among these are: How many human beings would it be good to have on the earth?

We have little information and less understanding about the psychosomatic results of crowding among human beings, but at present it appears that a population density as high as that in Harlem today is simply not good for people. Possibly we could devise some way to make it good, but the prospect does not look very promising.

In essence, we are dealing with qualitative and not quantitative questions, with the quality of human life and only incidentally with the quantity of people. In the long run, the Harvard Center for Population Studies will focus on the drama of living human beings, rather than on their entrances and their exits on the stage of life. We will be concerned with the physical health of human populations, with improvement of nutrition, reduction of vitality-sapping disease, and amelioration of genetic burdens.

We will be concerned with relating the education of human populations to the changing needs of individuals and their societies. We will want to find better ways to fit environments to human beings—not only the earthly environment of air, water, and land, but also the social environment created by interactions among men.

It is sometimes said that man is a wild animal. Though he has domesticated many other animals, he has never been able to domesticate himself. The underlying question for the Center for Population Studies is, "Can man domesticate himself?" Throughout most of his existence man was simply one among many species on the earth. But during the last few millennia he has pre-empted the planet, its space and its resources. Of far greater importance, we are perhaps the first form of matter in the twenty billion years of the lifetime of our galaxy that has had the ability to understand not only the world but itself. It does not seem too large a step from self-understanding to self-control.

3

HEADED FOR DISASTER

by Richard Lincoln

A graduate of Columbia University, Mr. Lincoln is a specialist in problems of population and has done extensive writing for Planned Parenthood-World Population.

Modern medical science is one triumphant achievement of man's intellect. It has brought us better health and longer life. Now that same transcendent intellect must be turned to the solution of some of the problems its achievements have created. One of these problems is the control of the vast destructive potentials of nuclear energy. Another such problem—equally vital to man's survival—is the control of our own human abundance.

We are now increasing at a rate that will cause the world's population to double every thirty-five years. At this pace, the world's present population of 3.3 billion will explode to more than seven billion by the century's end, and to sixteen billion by the year 2040.

Population growth, at anything near current rates, *is* something new under the sun. Modern medicine and sanitation have enabled more people to live longer and have more children. Typical is the case of Ceylon, where the introduction of DDT was largely responsible in less than a decade for a 57 per cent decline in the death rate, a population increase of 83 per cent, *and a resultant steady decline in per capita income.* Thus, death control, however welcome, has not been an unmixed blessing for many—even most—of the world's people, whose high childbearing rates—through lack of birth control—continue business as usual, but the fruits of whose much heralded revolution of rising expectations recede farther into the distance.

Nor is this problem restricted to far-off places. Preliminary results of a pioneering study made under Planned Parenthood auspices by the University of Pittsburgh's Center for Regional Economic Studies show that without more birth control, the number of unemployable people in the United States will rise, the total tax burden will continue to grow, there will be continued chronic dependency, and the economy will be hard-pressed to maintain improving standards of living. On the other hand, if Americans are given the birth control help they desire, we will have a relatively smaller, better educated population that is better equipped to take a productive role in our developing society.

Overpopulation is not the only problem confronting mankind in this critical period. We must find ways to speed up economic development, to find more food for the mounting numbers of underfed billions, to educate today's children for tomorrow's world, to eradicate the killer diseases, to find ways that we may live together in peace, as individuals and as nations.

But besides all these, even necessary if we are to hope for their achievement, as world authorities and leaders of all religious faiths now agree, we must bring the message and the means of voluntary fertility control to the hundreds of millions of ignorant and poverty-ridden families who are today without them.

The results of intensive birth control programs among America's and the world's poor are just coming in. But thus far the evidence is overwhelming. Voluntary birth control is reducing birth rates, as proven by experience in many countries. Given the knowledge and the means, couples everywhere, whether Indian villagers or Chicago slum dwellers, eagerly embrace the opportunity to limit their families and improve their lot.

Yet, in terms of the magnitude of America's population problems and the world's population crisis, we have barely begun. There are at least four and a half of America's five million poor and fertile families who have not yet been given the opportunity to limit family size according to their own wishes. Abroad, there are hundreds of millions of families who need birth control help, but who have not yet been reached. And there is not much time left. There are nearly three-hundred-thousand babies born every day, two thirds of them into families that are poor, hungry, ignorant, ill.

The cost of a runaway population growth—whether in Asia, Africa, Latin American, or in the backwaters of our American cities and suburbs—is deeply disturbing when recorded in dollars and cents. More intangible, but perhaps more important, is the terrible cost in human suffering, ignorance, and illness to individuals and families; family planning allows them to give their children the warm welcome in a loving home, the healthy opportunity for education, employment, and fulfillment that should be every child's birthright.

A world where people can have the number of children they want and can care for, rather than any number of children that they don't know how to prevent, will be a more prosperous world, a better and safer world for business. The alternative, a world without birth regulation, where population and poverty unchecked continue to explode is —like nuclear holocaust—unthinkable if civilization, as we know it, is to survive.

"Our entire concept of a healthy and a happy world at peace," says Marriner S. Eccles, former chairman of the Federal Reserve Board, "with pestilence and premature death eradicated, is totally unrealistic unless we recognize the limitations of population growth that must be imposed on ourselves, as well as the rest of the world. We cannot hope to live in this age much longer, enjoying security and abundance with a congested poverty-stricken world around us."

Stressing this point, Aldous Huxley points out: "To anyone who thinks in biological as well as in economic, political, and sociological terms, it is self-evident that a society which practices death control must at the same time practice birth control."

Thirty-five years ago, one third of the world's people lived in the impoverished areas of Africa, Asia, and Latin America. Today, 2.4 billion people, nearly three fourths of the world's population, live in these developing nations. In fifteen years, they will be 3.4 billions— equivalent to the entire population of the world today. And thirty-five years from now, if current trends continue, there will be more than six billion Africans, Asians, and Latin Americans—85 per cent of the world's population—their hopes for even moderate affluence, education, health, and dignity still frustrated.

The peoples of these developing nations are desperately poor. Three fourths of them (more than half the world's people) earn less than $100 a year, and 94 per cent earn less than $275. Tomorrow, presuming births as usual, the poor will be comparatively poorer. With luck, the average per capita income of the six billion Africans, Asians, and Latin Americans at the century's end might approach $250. Today, in the United States, per capita annual income is more than $2500, and is increasing at a rate of about 6 per cent each year.

The world's hungry people are producing more children than food to feed them. World food production, according to the UN's Food and Agriculture Organization (FAO), lagged last year behind population growth.

In Africa, Latin America, and the Far East, food production is growing only two thirds as fast as population. And in the latter two areas, per capita food production is still *below* the levels attained twenty-five years ago.

Not only the amount of food per person but its nutritional content has fallen in developing countries. Since World War II, these nations have suffered a 6 per cent *decrease* in protein consumption, while there has been a comparable *increase* in the developed areas, UN figures show.

The FAO World Food Survey of 1963 found that at least 60 per cent of the people in the less developed areas are undernourished, and that half the world suffers from hunger, malnutrition—or both.

There are more mouths to feed but fewer hands proportionately to produce. The sharp decline in infant mortality brought about by modern medical science has resulted in a drastic increase in the percentage of nonproductive children under fifteen in the less developed countries. These now range from 40 to 45 per cent, compared with 20 to 30 per cent in the developed countries. If high rates of fertility in the less developed countries are not curbed, the crushing extra burden of child dependency will continue into the next century.

There is almost no money left over for investment. Rapid population growth and the heavy burden of child dependency divert savings to production of immediate necessities for subsistence: food, clothing, shelter. Individual families are able to save little or nothing, and the savings by corporations and through government taxation are always inadequate for investment in such projects as hydroelectric power plants, mechanized farms, and factories needed to improve living standards and achieve modernization.

In Latin America, for example, from 1950 to 1960, investment did not grow at all in relation to the domestic product, and it has declined each year *since* 1960; while population has been rising annually by nearly 3 per cent.

Because of breakaway population growth, the less developed nations must run as fast as they can just to stand still. Thus, although gross domestic product from 1955 to 1960 grew in the developing countries at a rate nearly two times *higher* than in the developed economies, the growth of product per capita was lower, according to the UN.

"The magnitude of the problem is staggering," said the late President John F. Kennedy. "In Latin America, for example, population growth is already threatening to outpace economic growth—and in some parts of the continent living standards are actually declining. . . . The problems are no less serious or demanding in other developing nations of the world."

In addition, as population has gone up, production per capita has slowed down. The UN reports that the rate of growth of the per capita product in the developing countries averaged 2.5 per cent annually between 1950 and 1955; slipped to 1.9 per cent from 1955 to 1960; and is now at about 1 per cent. In many of these countries, and in Latin America as a whole, annual per capita product has now begun to decline.

Because high rates of population growth have drastically slowed down economic development, the real dollar gap between the incomes of the peoples of the developed and developing economies widens at accelerating rates. Thus, in the decade 1953 to 1963, according to the FAO, average income per person in the less developed countries with high population growth rose by only one dollar a year; while in the developed economies, it rose by some $30 per head. Americans spent more per capita on recreation last year than the average African or Asian received as his entire year's income. Thus, the disparity grows between the *hopes* of the peoples of Asia, Africa, and Latin America for a better life and the *reality* of increased poverty, crowding, and economic stagnation.

After traveling extensively through the developing countries, John Gunther wrote: "Foreign aid cannot be successful in the long run in raising living standards, which is its primary object, unless population growth in the countries concerned levels off. We're caught on a vast, hideous treadmill. . . . The more aid we give, the more we shall have to keep on giving, because of relentless population pressure."

The governments of most developing countries have invested a very large proportion of their scanty savings in education, with the aim of reducing illiteracy and making their populations, in the long run, more productive. A great many countries have substantially increased the numbers of children enrolled in school, while the actual numbers still denied an education may also have risen.

For the developing countries as a whole, despite vast adult education programs to wipe out illiteracy, the number of illiterates has not declined, and may have gone up since the 1950 estimate of 700 million persons. Thus, poverty, ignorance, illiteracy perpetuate themselves as the population multiplies beyond the capacities of poor countries to invest sufficiently in schools and teachers.

Housing shortages and substandard housing, always serious problems in the developing countries, continue to rise under the relentless pressures of population growth and migration to the large cities. This has led to the mushrooming of squatter's settlements, bidonvilles, favelas, shantytowns in and surrounding almost all of the cities of Africa, Asia, and Latin America. According to the Social Progress Trust Fund of the Inter-American Development Bank, more than 50 per cent of Latin America's urban population, and a vastly greater proportion of the rural population, live in dwellings that do not meet minimal standards for human habitation. The situation is even more acute in Asia and Africa. A recent U.N. study of West Africa's housing needs and problems seriously questions whether, considering current population and economic trends, the mass of African people can ever be housed.

"The population explosion," pointed out George W. Ball, U. S. Undersecretary of State, "will place an ever-increasing burden on the more advanced countries and international lending institutions [for providing capital and technical skills]. It will place a burden as well on the developing countries . . . in mobilizing internal resources for development."

The UN secretary-general reported on the results of an inquiry among governments on economic problems resulting from population growth. The report noted that most of the governments of developing countries considered their high rates of population growth "an important handicap to economic and social development." Here is what some of these countries are saying:

Ceylon: The accelerated increase in population imposes a serious strain on the limited resources of the country and prevents any substantial expansion in the economy.

Colombia: Even where they show increases, the basic economic indices have not kept pace with the steady growth of population.

Guatemala: The spontaneous growth of the country's economic development has not been sufficient to meet the needs arising from the natural increase in population.

Jamaica: Population growth threatens to nullify the gains from development.

Panama: As a result of the declining death rate and high fertility, the rate of population growth has increased, unaccompanied by economic changes capable of producing a sufficient increase in per capita income.

Gamal Abdel Nasser, President, U.A.R.: The population increase constitutes the most dangerous obstacle that faces the Egyptian people in their drive towards raising the standards of production in their country in an effective and efficient way.

Muhammad Ayub Khan, President, Pakistan: If we continue to increase at the present rate it will ultimately lead to a standard of living little better than that of animals. . . . Planned parenthood is a vital problem for countries like Pakistan.

Habib Bourguiba, President, Tunisia: The people must become aware of the problem. For that I am counting on a nationwide campaign . . . in the cities and in the countryside. We must cut down the birth rate.

Jawaharlal Nehru, India: For us in India, it is of the utmost importance . . . that we should make this movement for population control by family planning a widespread and successful one.

Birth control *can* have a profound effect on raising living standards in less developed countries. The National Academy of Sciences reports that a gradual reduction in the rate of childbearing in these countries, totaling 50 per cent in thirty years, would add about 40 per cent to the income per capita that should be achieved by then.

The United Nations Economic Commission for Latin America predicts that if birth rates continue to rise to a peak of 3.5 per cent per year on that continent, the chronically improverished portion of the urban population will grow from one third to one half in twenty years. On the other hand, a reduction of annual population growth to 2 per cent would bring about the complete absorption of this marginal group into the productive work force in that period.

From Hong Kong to Barbados, families have indicated consistently that they *want* to limit family size; given adequate information and suitable means, they will do so.

In India, women patients in eight government health clinics in Delhi showed an 85 per cent decrease in the pregnancy rate as the result of a three-year intensive birth regulation program. Birth control efforts in selected districts of Taiwan resulted in a 60 per cent birth rate decline in those areas.

A similar program in Korea produced a 20 per cent decline *during the first year* in test areas. In one year, Barbados' birth control program reduced the birth rate of the entire island by 16 per cent. Hong Kong reduced its birth rate through voluntary birth regulation programs by 16 per cent. Singapore's program resulted in a 26 per cent decline in the birth rate.

Summing up the story of the need for some effective means of regulating the world's exploding population, Lammot du Pont Copeland says: "In the very abundance of swelling human numbers, the poverty of most of mankind is rooted. This truth, in the short arc of a dozen years, has etched itself deeply into the minds of scholars and physicians, priests and presidents, leaders of industry and science. From the Nobel laureate to the thoughtful businessman, leaders everywhere of all faiths now recognize that birth control is an essential part of any humane design to raise living standards around the world—and to keep them high here at home."

4

THE FACTS OF LIFE

by John Nuveen

Mr. Nuveen has been actively associated with several organizations interested in the population problem. He was
a delegate to the First Pan-American Assembly on Population, held in Cali, Colombia, in August 1965. In the years
immediately following World War II, he served as chairman of Economic Recovery Missions in Europe.

An Anglican minister, Thomas Robert Malthus, in *An Essay on the
Principles of Population,* published in 1798, observed that population
increases by geometric ratio while the means of subsistence increase
by arithmetic ratio. He concluded that ultimately there would be more
people than food and that, unless the population was reduced by war
and disease, famine would take over—not a very pleasant prospect. The
first attempts at projecting when this dire situation would come about
were based on insufficient knowledge of world resources and agricultural science; hence Malthus' conclusions became discredited for a
time in popular thought.

But let us examine Malthus' principle. We can readily see the difference between arithmetic and geometric ratios by comparing an

arithmetic progression and a geometric progression which start from the same point and use the same constant, adding it in one case and multiplying with it in the other. For example, if we start with the figure 1 and add the figure 2 thirty times, an arithmetic progression will mount at the rate of 1, 3, 5, 7, 9, etc., to 61. But if we start with 1 and multiply by 2 thirty times, a geometric progression will mount at the rate of 1, 2, 4, 8, 16, etc., to 1,073,741,824.

If we chart these progressions on graph paper the way mathematicians like to do we will find that while the arithmetic progression is a straight line, the geometric progression is a curve which bends ever so slowly at first, then begins to turn upward at an accelerating rate, finally shooting up almost vertically. The graphs illustrate a mathematical law; namely, that no matter how high you start your arithmetic progression and how large a constant you use, and no matter how low you start your geometric progression and how small the constant you use, the geometric progression will overtake the arithmetic progression and soar beyond it.

If we accept Malthus' principle of arithmetic and geometric ratios of increase for means of subsistence and population respectively— and virtually all authorities do—we must conclude that it will never be possible to solve the problem by concentrating on increasing the production of food. We can postpone the problem but we can't solve it, and anyone who seriously suggests otherwise reveals ignorance of the laws of nature.

Perhaps the easiest way of understanding why concentrating on food production will not solve the population problem is to use a little simple arithmetic. If the rate of increase in world population remains the same as it is today, doubling every generation, our present 3.5 billion people will increase in thirty generations (900 years) to 3 sextillion, 758 quintillion, 96 quadrillion, 384 trillion people—4550 people living on each square foot of the earth's land surface.

But let's move from the realm of unreality to the area of the possible. Harrison Brown, in his book *The Challenge of Man's Future,* makes a studious effort to estimate how many people the earth could support. Assuming that we could capture all the energy in the sun's rays and utilize every resource, including the atomic energy in granite, he says—and his conclusion is the most optimistic anyone has come up with—that the earth could support fifty billion people if they would be satisfied to subsist on the products of algae farms and yeast factories. At the present rate of population increase we will have fifty billion people in four more generations (120 years).

Now to go from the theoretically possible to the practicably probable. A year and a half ago Raymond H. Ewell, vice-president of the State University of New York at Buffalo and former adviser to the governments of India and the Philippines, addressed a meeting of the American Chemical Society in Chicago. The lead paragraph of the newspaper report summarized his speech as follows: "The worst famine in history is just around the corner, and more than a billion persons in Africa, Asia and South America face starvation, a scientist warned here Tuesday."

Red China, India, and Pakistan, Dr. Ewell is reported to have predicted, will have famines of serious proportions in the 1970s. This fate will rapidly extend to more millions in Egypt, Iran, and Turkey and within ten years will spread to Africa and Latin America. By that time it will dwarf all the other problems we face. Further, Ewell said, the famine will be of massive proportions, affecting hundreds of millions, possibly billions, of persons. If this happens, as appears very probable, it will be the most colossal catastrophe ever to befall mankind.

Ewell is of the opinion that the only way to head off the famine is to begin now to increase grain production in the continents where even today the population is outrunning its food supply. He further states that control of the birth rate is the ultimate solution to the threat, but considers it unlikely that it could be made effective in time to avert the famine. "It is hard for us sitting here in rich, comfortable, overfed America to realize that the greatest disaster in the history of the world is just around the corner," he concludes. The headline on the front page of the New York *Times* for March 31, 1966—PRESIDENT ASKS BILLION FOR INDIA AS FAMINE RELIEF—is perhaps the first ominous warning that Ewell's frightening prophecy will be fulfilled.

At this point someone is probably asking, Why should we worry about India? Let her solve her own problems. And someone else is wondering whether we don't have enough resources in the United States so that we do not have to worry in our lifetime. Let's answer the second man first.

A privately endowed organization based in Washington, D.C., and called Resources for the Future is concerned with anticipating shortages which will affect our national economy. In 1963 some of the economists who work for this organization published *Resources in America's Future —Patterns of Requirements and Availabilities, 1960-2000.* This thick volume is the most comprehensive analysis to date on the adequacy of our resources to support the 330 million people that it is predicted we will have by the year 2000. A review of this work in the London *Economist,* whose detached position gives it desirable objectivity, concludes: "While the economists do not doubt that man has the ingenuity to make his life possible, they do question whether he has the common sense to keep it attractive and worth living."

Isn't that the real point? And shouldn't we be asking ourselves whether under our present scheme life is becoming more attractive and more worth living? Specifically, as urban sprawl takes over our countryside, is it becoming more or less attractive? As our cities become larger and more congested and buildings rise higher and higher to produce darker and deeper urban canyons, and traffic moves more and more slowly, is life becoming more or less attractive? As mechanized agriculture sends four fifths of our onetime farm population to the cities, is life more or less attractive for them? As automation cuts down the size of our industrial labor force at the rate of about six thousand jobs a day, are those who are let out—usually the less skilled and less educated—and their families going to find life more or less attractive? The riots in Watts on the West Coast and in Harlem on the East Coast are signs that for the bottom economic group in our society life may not be worth living.

All these situations are aggravated rather than helped by an over-rapid increase in population, and the burden of providing schools, dwellings, water, highways, etc., for our expanding population places on our economy and on our tax structure a load that is becoming ever more burdensome.

Now a few words to the man who questions our aid to India and indeed wonders why we should be concerned about world population problems. Today 80 per cent of our federal budget—80 per cent of our income taxes—goes to pay for past wars and to prepare for future wars. Our reluctant but unavoidable involvement in two world wars and a cold war and the unending threat of a third world war are the consequence of the failure of our past policies to deal with world problems that might have been solved by peaceful means before they developed into violent tensions and military conflict.

The greatest force pushing the world toward war today is the population explosion. As far back as 1957 John F. Kennedy, then a young senator, in a speech to the Economic Club of Chicago called attention to "the utterly unprecedented world population explosion" resulting "from a phenomenal reduction . . . of the death rate, from the control of infectious diseases, sanitation improvement, medical progress . . ." He pointed out that "the standard of living for much of the world is declining, [the poor nations'] poverty and economic backwardness are increasing, and their share of the world's population is growing."

The widening economic gap between the rich and poor nations, he concluded, "is a matter of war and peace, of national security, of stopping the advance of communism." And as President he again called attention to the population dilemma. "The magnitude of the problem is staggering," he declared in his Special Message to Congress on Foreign Aid in March 1961.

The obvious way to deal with these problems is by programs for birth control that will match our successful efforts in the last generation at death control. Here, however, we run into religious opposition. Thus far it has been the policy of almost every organization concerned with the population problem to ignore the religious aspect of the matter. I think it is very unrealistic to do so. For one thing, it is unrealistic to attempt to raise the standard of living in underdeveloped countries —ostensibly the purpose of our foreign aid programs—by merely giving them economic and technical assistance to increase their total production.

The measure of the standard of living is a simple quotient: total production divided by the number of people. Because of the danger of religious controversy, the public officials who formulate and administer foreign aid programs have made no provision for dealing with the population problem, with the result that in many countries the population has increased as fast as, if not faster than, economic production. Hence the standard of living has not risen appreciably and in some cases has actually been lowered, to the defeat of our purpose and the waste of billions of dollars.

At home, it is unrealistic to try to deal with the problem of children who are without families or whose families cannot afford to rear them properly by a federally supported program of Aid to Dependent Children. The problem and its costs have been mounting year after year. It is obvious that it could be largely cured at the source by a program of assisting in the prevention of the birth of unwanted children, who comprise the largest group in the ranks of dependent children. This is only one of many problems related to population that are raising our taxes and making life less attractive for many of our citizens.

The religious opposition that is hampering efforts to deal with population problems emanates largely, but not exclusively, from a minority in the hierarchy of the Roman Catholic Church. Through the centuries there has been perhaps no other single institution which has prevented or alleviated suffering among mankind to as great a degree as the Roman Catholic Church. Its missions, its hospitals, and its devoted members have ministered to millions. But if the Catholic Church continues to oppose effective measures for dealing with population growth, and if Dr. Ewell's predictions of world famine are fulfilled, as it now seems they will be, the Catholic Church may within two decades have to face the accusation of causing more suffering through starvation than any other single institution in the world, and to many more millions than it has helped in the past.

There are a few simple statements that should be made about the religious controversy over birth control. First, among all the world's major religions, it is only in Christianity that there is any important opposition to birth control. Our Judeo-Christian heritage with its emphasis on the dignity and sacredness of the individual has resulted in the development of our human resources to a degree that has given us the highest standard of living in the world. But in regarding human life as sacred, that heritage presents us with the theological problem of determining at just what point it becomes sacred, and of deciding whether the lives of those in some stage of prenatal development are more important than the lives of those already living when we arrive at the point where the world cannot support both groups.

Second, every Christian denomination facing these problems has at one time or another in the past opposed birth control, but practically all of them except the Roman Catholics have withdrawn their opposition in the light of the changes we have wrought in the world and of the new knowledge we have discovered.

Third, the difficulties of the Catholic Church are probably more in-

stitutional than theological, in that those who must make the pronouncements are usually older men for whom change is more difficult
to accept. One of my favorite sayings is that you can judge your age
by the amount of pain you feel when you come in contact with a new
idea. The delays of the Church in accepting the scientific views of
Copernicus and Galileo were not too important in their direct effect
on mankind. But delays today in facing the changes which have produced the world population explosion can cause unimaginable disaster.

Germane to this discussion is a two-volume work published in 1896
under the authorship of Andrew D. White, the first president of Cornell
University and the man who interested Ezra Cornell in putting up the
money to found the university as primarily a scientific institution and
then discovered that he had to defend the fact that it was not af-
filiated with any religious denomination. White's book, *A History of
the Warfare of Science with Theology in Christendom,* is exciting reading. It has been recently reprinted in one volume and I commend it
to you. Its thesis is stated in the introduction: "In all modern history,
interference with science in the supposed interest of religion, no matter how conscientious such interference may have been, has resulted in
the direst evils both to religion and to science, and invariably; and, on
the other hand, all untrammelled scientific investigation, no matter how
dangerous to religion some of its stages may have seemed for the time
to be, has invariably resulted in the highest good both of religion and
of science."

These words suggest that those who speak out for change in the
position of the Roman Catholic Church may be contributing to the
highest good of that Church and of religion, and, alternately, that those
who remain silent may be doing a disservice both to the Catholic
Church and to religion.

The problem of birth control is urgent. World population is increasing at the rate of 1,300,000 a week—up from only 800,000 ten years
ago—and most of this increase is in the nations where, Raymond Ewell
predicts, there will be famines running into starvation for millions and
hundreds of millions in the next two decades. Every week we put off
supporting the efforts that are being made to deal with this international
problem constructively, we ensure greater disaster for mankind. Every
week we put off supporting some organization which is concerned with

the population problem in this country, we make it less certain that we will have the internal strength to deal with violence from without produced by world tensions inflamed by famine, and that we will be able to keep life attractive and worth living for our descendants in the great land we have inherited.

Part II
FAMILY PLANNING

5

RESPONSIBLE PARENTHOOD

by John A. O'Brien

How are we to deal effectively with the problem of a population increasing with a speed unprecedented in history? It is especially acute in the underdeveloped countries where the population is exploding, if not like bombs, at least like giant firecrackers. This is the question confronting not only the United States of America but also the other nations of the free world.

New developments and a more penetrating analysis of the pluralistic nature of the society in which we live offer well-founded hope for the co-operative action so desperately needed to solve this problem on both the national and international levels. Let us first examine the large area of agreement on responsible parenthood and see if the differences cannot be further narrowed without compromise of conscience.

Contrary to widespread belief, the Catholic Church does not forbid birth regulation. For any serious cause a married couple is exempt from the normal obligation of parenthood for a long time and even for the whole duration of married life. The method sanctioned is rhythm, the use of the infertile or safe period. If the currently available means for predicting or ascertaining the time of ovulation—the calendar record of menstrual periods, basal temperature chart, and test tape—are carefully employed, the rhythm method is estimated to achieve a fair degree

45

of reliability. Pope Pius XII expressed the hope that further research will increase still more its effectiveness.

Thus John C. Ford, S.J., and Gerald Kelly, S.J., state that Catholics as well as Protestants are today stressing responsible parenthood, which the authors term "a serious business." They point out that the duty to procreate, traditionally insisted on by the Church, is a limited one and that "one measure of the duty as far as legal justice and piety to the race are concerned is the population *need* of the time.

"When this suggestion of an inherent limit to the obligation was first made, the best social scientists seemed to think that fertile couples should have four or five children in order to make provision for the conservation and slight increase of the human race. Since then, with increased consciousness of the population problem, this number has been slightly reduced, at least for some countries. For instance, it has been estimated that a family of three children would sufficiently provide for the needs of the United States."

What about the traditional attitude which considered that the size of a family was a matter to be determined by God and not by man? The discovery of the sterile period has vastly enlarged the sphere of human providence. "That there exists this widened area of personal decision making," point out Ford and Kelly, "is simply a fact that can no longer be disregarded or evaded. Given a situation where the number of the children is a serious practical problem, if there exists a legitimate, effective, and reasonably available method of regulating the size of the family, Christian prudence requires that this method must be taken into consideration along with other factors when these personal decisions are to be made.

"Man's reason makes him share in divine providence in a special way. When reason makes new discoveries of a morally acceptable kind, he must use his reason to plan his own life accordingly. This very use of reason is in accordance with divine providence. In fact it is not a case of human *versus* divine, but human providence sharing in the divine."

As a consequence of the enlargement of the area of personal decision making, couples are expected to use their intelligence in the planning of their families. "There are many cases today," point out Ford and Kelly, "when it is no longer the part of prudence to put the whole problem of family planning in the hands of God. And the more effective periodic continence becomes for larger numbers of people, the more will we have to reconsider our attitudes towards the respective roles of human and divine providence in this matter."

The necessity of such reconsideration became inevitable in 1951 when Pope Pius XII referred to "the legitimacy and, at the same time, the limits—in truth very wide—of a regulation of offspring, which, unlike so-called 'birth control,' is compatible with the law of God."

This was the keynote sounded by Father William J. Gibbons, S.J., professor of sociology at Fordham University, at a meeting of the Catholic Sociological Society in St. Louis in September 1961. He declared that Catholics in the United States have been oversold on procreation and undereducated on the responsibilities it entails. He believes that too many Catholics think they are being virtuous if they merely refrain from using contraceptives. He points out that the size of the family "should take into account the physical and mental health of the parents, their economic condition, and the society in which they live. When you are faced with such problems as overcrowding, lack of work opportunities, and the rest, you need to retreat."

Similarly Dr. Robert Odenwald, formerly professor of psychiatry at the Catholic University, points out that in the past too many Catholics have tended to follow, almost blindly, the biblical command to "increase and multiply." But in the light of the new knowledge and because of changing social and economic condtions, "the accent today is rightly placed on responsible parenthood."

"If cogent reasons indicate a limitation of family size," says Monsignor John A. Goodwine, theological censor for the New York archdiocese, "there should be no difficulty in admitting that the avoidance of pregnancy would be within the bounds of reason and morality." He remarks that the significant change in Catholic thinking on family size that has taken place in the last dozen years "does not seem to be sufficiently understood."

Similar, too, is the note sounded by Dom Gregory Stevens, O.S.B., professor of moral theology at the Catholic University. Pointing out that the common notion that the Church favors "absolutely a high birth rate" is false, he says: "Indiscriminate procreation is no moral ideal but mere irresponsibility, for the family must make prudent provision for the future welfare of the children both spiritually and physically. The Church considers the primary goal of the natural institution of matrimony to be that of *responsible parenthood.*

To help parents realize their responsibility, Dom Stevens points out that they "must take into account the present and *foreseeable* future conditions of society. This is demanded for the sake of the children themselves as well as for the common good which all are strictly bound to promote as a matter of what St. Thomas called general justice."

Equally concerned that married couples understand their responsibility in the light of a soaring population, Father Charles J. Corcoran, C.S.C., for many years professor of theology at Holy Cross College, Washington, D.C., warns: "It is unfortunate that in the debates on family limitation, many Catholics forget that the right use of marital rights implies more than the willingness to procreate a child. It implies not only the willingness but also the *ability* to provide for the child's material and spiritual welfare. Correctly understood, this grave responsibility should serve as a potent check on an undisciplined, even if biologically proper, use of sex."

Reflecting this new emphasis upon parental responsibility, Dr. John J. Kane, of the department of sociology at the University of Notre Dame, states: "Recent and tremendous social changes in the fields of education, economics, and family life place greater strains on American parents than they have perhaps ever faced in the past. Children's expectations have risen dramatically and parents' hopes of meeting such expectations are perhaps stronger than ever. All of this means that the very large family patterns typical of the early part of this century can no longer be realized by most parents if they hope to meet their *real responsibilities.* . . . Considerable thought will have to be given . . . to the practice of some type of family *limitation* in the majority of cases."

Equally explicit is the conclusion reached by Father John L. Thomas, S.J., sociologist of St. Louis University and a recognized authority on marriage and the family: "Granted present nuptiality rates, age at marriage, and advances in health care, no country can long make reasonable provision for its population increase unless a good percentage of its couples take some effective steps to regulate family size."

The stress placed by Catholic theologians, sociologists, and psychiatrists in America in recent years is mirrored in the writings of their European counterparts. In a recent scholarly work, *Love and Control,* Leon Joseph Cardinal Suenens, archbishop of Malines-Brussels, points out that conjugal love should be guided by reason and a clear consciousness of the duties of parenthood. Procreation should not be a matter of blind instinct. "One of the first and essential things to consider," he says, "when they [married couples] evaluate their circumstances in life is the education and training to give their children." He commends family planning and points out that it can "help a mother get used to the duties of motherhood in a more balanced way and aid her in taking on responsibilities with a greater reserve of generosity and, at the same time, more physical strength."

In an address at the Symposium on Christian Marriage in the Age of Vatican Council II in Washington, D.C., in November 1966, Father Henri de Riedmatten, O.P., secretary of the Pontifical Study Commission on Family, Population, and Birth Problems, told a large assembly of parish priests that the new concept of parental responsibility enriches pastoral theology. He explained that responsible parenthood, correctly understood, is a thoroughly Christian concept but one which has undergone significant development in modern years.

"Responsible parenthood in itself," he said, "says no more than what is a self-evident moral principle: Human reproduction is a responsible act, an eminently moral act." Acknowledging that some theologians have been hesitant to assimilate the notion of responsible parenthood into a complete theology of marriage, he said it would be most regrettable if they allowed false fears to "stand in the way of the tremendous enrichment which the doctrinal and pastoral theology of marriage can receive at precisely this point."

"Can we not illustrate very well the psychological impact of this acquisition in imagining what it would mean to the adolescent, once he had been initiated into the mysteries of life, to realize that he was not just the more or less consciously desired fruit of the marital intimacy of his parents, but rather the object of their clear and deliberate choice of will to bring him into the world?" he asked. He indicated that such deliberate prudent choice might in many cases be an improvement over the "we'll take as many children as the Lord sends us" attitude.

The Dominican scholar pointed out that each time the parents decide to procreate they should take into consideration not only the obligations which they will have to their baby but also the duties they have to their existing children. Even if the parents are willing to go far in the sacrifices they might accept for themselves in calling new life into existence, they should not impose sacrifices in the same measure upon their other children. The parents must be careful, he stressed, not to upset the delicate balance within the development of the children they already have and they should be certain that this development is assured in both a material and spiritual sense.

Father Stanislas de Lestapis, S.J., professor at the Catholic Institute of Paris and the Vatican's representative at the United Nations World Population Conference in Rome in 1954, says that "there is, in principle, a right or, better, a duty, to practice a form of birth limitation based on careful thought. . . . There is an optimum number for each family and each family alone can judge what it is."

The Belgian demographer, Clement Mertens, S.J., of St. Albert College in Louvain, calls attention to the "increasing awareness among the leaders of the Church, and among theologians, moralists, and others, of the problems which large families now have to face. And there is an increasing awareness of the problems countries have to face where the population is increasing quickly." He acknowledges that instructions on birth regulation on the pastoral level are not without risks and difficulties.

Nevertheless, he points out: "Risks and difficulties do not justify inertia. . . . It is the duty of the ecclesiastical authorities in each country to face the problem and see that competent laymen, especially in the best universities, proceed with research which will permit them to cope with different given situations, according to regions or social classes, and to adopt means which will reach a solution."

Probably no other country in Europe has felt so acutely the pressure of population as Holland. This is reflected in the candor, understanding, and sympathy with which the Dutch bishops have discussed the difficult problems facing married couples today. Speaking on a television program in April 1963, Bishop William M. Bekkers of 's-Hertogenbosch explained that not everyone can reach at once the ideal in marital virtue.

"Those who have entered Christian matrimony," said Bishop Bekkers, "have received from God and under His blessing a mandate of life which is focussed first on leading one life together in conjugal love and secondly on founding and building together a good family. Science and its discoveries have enabled man to regulate human reproduction. The birth rate now falls within man's responsibility. One can even say that birth regulation, which is quite different from [contraceptive] birth control, is a normal part of the total task of a married couple."

Bishop Bekkers then pointed out that only the married couple is in a position to determine the number of offspring they can properly rear and educate. This is within the competence of their conscience, and no outsider can interfere with their decision. A physician or a spiritual adviser must respect the private conscience.

Recognizing the imperfections of the rhythm system, the bishop said: "Not even the rhythm method is without objections. For many people the rhythm method is a solution, but we also know that it causes insuperable difficulties for many others. We understand that there are situations where one cannot consider all Christian and human values at the same time. In that case the Church does not immediately think of egoism or luxury.

"She knows that married couples, in well-intentioned love for each other and for their families, sometimes take steps which cannot be considered right steps in the eyes of the Church. But the Church also knows that what one person can reach cannot always be reached by others. She wants to give room for a gradual, perhaps slow and imperfect growing, like that which is possible in all other areas of life—in charity, honesty, and piety."

These scholars are but echoing the thoughts expressed by Pope Pius XII on the Feast of the Epiphany in 1957: "When the infant comes into the world, he must have a home to receive him—a home capable of providing him in good health—and to assist him in acquiring those faculties of mind and heart that will enable him to take his proper place in society when the time comes."

Vatican Council II stresses the importance of parental responsibility in the procreation of offspring. In its constitution on *The Church in the Modern World* the Council declares that parents are to "fulfill their tasks with human and Christian responsibility. With docile reverence toward God, they will come to the right decision by common counsel and effort. They will thoughtfully take into account both their own welfare and that of their children, those already born and those which may be foreseen. For this accounting they will reckon with both the material and the spiritual conditions of the times as well as of their state in life. Finally, they will consult the interests of the family group, of temporal society, and of the Church herself."

Who are to decide the number of children a married couple should have? No one but the parents themselves should make this decision, for they best know the conditions of their health and finances. The Council is emphatic in reserving this right to the parents. "The parents themselves," it declares, "should ultimately make this judgment in the sight of God." Furthermore the Council restored the balance that has often been lost by an overemphasis on procreation. It brings out the rich personal values of mutual love, which are of paramount importance in marriage, and those values can exist even when there are no children.

"Marriage to be sure," declares the Council, "is not instituted solely for procreation. Rather, its very nature as an unbreakable compact between persons, and the welfare of the children, both demand that the mutual love of the spouses, too, be embodied in a rightly ordered manner, that it grow and ripen. Therefore, marriage persists as a whole manner and communion of life, and maintains its value and indissolubility, even when offspring are lacking—despite, rather often, the very intense desire of the couple."

Similar is the emphasis placed by Protestant Churches in recent years upon responsible parenthood. In a statement on *Responsible Parenthood* issued in 1961 by the National Council of Churches, responsible parenthood is described as weighing "the claims of procreation and the situation of the family in society. In determining the number and frequency of offspring the parents should give careful consideration to the following four factors:

"1. The right of the child to be wanted, loved, cared for, educated, and trained in the 'discipline and instruction of the Lord' (Ephesians 6:4). The rights of existing children to parental care have a proper claim. 2. The prospects for health of a future child, if medical and eugenic evidence seem negatively conclusive. 3. The health and welfare of the mother-wife, and the need for the spacing of children to safeguard them. 4. The social situation, when rapid population growth places dangerous pressures on the means of livelihood and endangers the social order."

The statement tells parents to remember "that having children is a venture in faith, requiring a measure of courage and confidence in God's goodness. Too cautious a reckoning of the costs may be as great an error as failure to lift the God-given power of procreation to the level of ethical decision."

Probably no religious faith places greater emphasis upon the responsibility of parenthood than Judaism. Reflecting this stress, Rabbi Albert M. Shulman, chairman of the Commission on Marriage, Family, and the Home of the Central Conference of American Rabbis, says: "Parents have the serious obligation of regulating the size of their family so they will be able to provide properly for the health and education of their offspring. Procreation should not be a matter of blind instinct but of intelligent and careful planning. This is not only a social obligation but also a moral and religious one."

Re-echoing the note sounded by Jewish religious leaders, Rabbi David H. Wilce declares: "The concept of the sanctity of life is enhanced and the holiness of marriage is given a new dimension when parenthood is freely elected, when children are born wanted, and when family size is determined by conditions of health and well-being for the individual family and for society."

The factors listed in the statements of the National Council of Churches and of Jewish religious leaders are much the same as those which Catholic theologians and sociologists are likewise stressing in their description of responsible parenthood. Here then is a vast area of crucial and strategic importance, where Protestants, Catholics, and Jews are in substantial agreement. Here they can work together, with each group following its conscience, to achieve the same important goal.

Here is a key which, if properly used, is capable of opening the door to constructive action in solving the population problem on the national and international levels. That key embodies the two crucial elements to make it work: the prudent *regulation* of births and the clear consciousness of the *responsibility* they entail, which is but another name for family planning.

6

BIRTH CONTROL:
THE ONLY ANSWER

by Raymond Ewell

Dr. Ewell is vice-president for research, State University
of New York at Buffalo. A chemical engineer by original
training, he is an economist by professional evolution. He
has been a consultant to several United States government agencies, international organizations, and foreign
governments. His conclusions on the population problem
are based on observations in most of the countries of
Asia and some in Africa and Latin America over the past
twenty-six years. He is particularly familiar with conditions in India, Pakistan, the Philippines, and Egypt.

More information on fertility control, or birth control to use a more
direct term, is needed so that men and women all over the world can
plan the number and spacing of their children—sensibly, safely, and
certainly. The vast majority of the married couples in the world today
do not know how to plan the number and spacing of their children.
They simply do not have the information on how this can be done.
Even in the United States literally millions of married couples do not

have this information. And yet surveys have shown that most married couples in many countries would like to be able to plan the number and spacing of the children they have.

There are many personal reasons for this desire. Economic reasons predominate, but there are also psychological, medical, and other reasons. Most couples get married because they want to have children, but there are good and sufficient reasons why most couples want to limit the number and plan the spacing of the children they bring into the world. This is the personal, human reason why more information on birth control is needed.

However, in a broader social and political context, more information on birth control is needed because:

1. The world is running out of space, i.e., good-quality living space
2. The world is running out of food.
3. The world is running out of fresh, drinkable water and even running out of fresh air fit for breathing in many areas.
4. The world is using up its irreplaceable resources at rapidly increasing rates.
5. The increasing population densities of many countries, including the United States, are causing many social problems of steadily increasing magnitudes.

During the past year we have heard an increasing amount of talk and publicity on many problems associated with our increasing population in the United States—increased crime, juvenile delinquency, water pollution, air pollution, urban deterioration, noise, dirt, waste disposal, racial friction, and others. Increased population is not the sole cause of these social problems, but in all cases it is a major factor.

But even these problems, which seem important to us in the United States, fade into relative insignificance compared to the food problem faced by many countries. The very real threat of mass starvation within the next ten to fifteen years hangs over the 2.5 billion human beings of Asia, Africa, and Latin America. *This is the biggest, most fundamental and most nearly insoluble problem that has ever faced the human race.* And it is a problem with definite implications and responsibilities for the medical profession.

The world food problem is of such staggering proportions and such complexity that it is difficult to grasp it until one has observed it and studied it over a period of time. Moreover, it is almost impossible to understand this problem unless one has spent at least some time in Asia, where poverty and undernutrition reach their greatest depths. Starvation is not a problem in the United States, nor will it be for the foreseeable future, nor is it a problem in Europe, the Soviet Union, Canada, Australia, or New Zealand. But it is a very real problem in most of the countries of the three poor continents of Asia, Africa, and Latin America. The populations of these continents are growing rapidly, at the highest growth rates in history, and the production of food is lagging behind the population growth. This is the problem in a nutshell.

If present trends continue, it seems likely that famine will reach serious proportions in India, Pakistan, and Communist China in the early 1970s. Indonesia, Iran, Turkey, Egypt, Brazil, and several other countries will follow within a few years. And most of the other countries of Asia, Africa, and Latin America will fall in this category by 1980. Such a famine will be of massive proportions affecting hundreds of millions, possibly even billions, of persons.

If this happens, as now appears probable, it will be the most colossal catastrophe in history. It would be a completely new situation in the world's history—not enough food for the billions of human beings inhabiting the surface of this globe. This would be the Malthusian doctrine finally coming true after 170 years.

In my opinion, the food/population problem will be the overriding problem of the last quarter of this century. I anticipate that it will completely overshadow such political problems as Vietnam, Cuba, the Congo, Kashmir, Berlin, and others, which loom so large at the present time. The political and economic consequences of widespread famine in Asia, Africa, and Latin America are certain to be massive and far-reaching. *It seems unlikely that stable governments can be maintained in countries where a large part of the population is starving.*

In order to emphasize how explosive the "population explosion" really is, let us consider three dates—1830, 1930, and 2030. The population of the world in 1830 was approximately one billion, a hundred years later in 1930 it was two billion, but if present population growth trends should continue, the world's population in 2030 would be fourteen billion. Let me repeat, if present population trends continue, the world would have a fourteen billion population in the year 2030! The year 2030 may seem a long time off, but most readers of this book will have children and grandchildren living in 2030. Obviously there will be many changes in the world's social structure before 2030, and frankly I doubt if the population of the world will ever reach fourteen billion—as a result of starvation if for no other reason. But the possibility that there might be fourteen billion people in the world in 2030 is something to think about.

However, let us get out of the realm of fantasy and focus on reality, namely, on the year 1980; 1980 is a year that is just around the corner when you think back to 1950, which seems only yesterday. The population of the world in mid-1965 was about 3.4 billion and growing at about seventy million per year. In the fifteen years between 1965 and 1980, the world's population will increase by at least 1.2 billion—from 3.4 billion in 1965 to 4.6 billion in 1980. This population growth is almost a certainty—in fact, it could be even greater. The mothers who will bear these children are already here.

Most of this tremendous increase in population will occur in Asia, Africa, and Latin America, in fact, about one billion out of 1.2 billion. Only 200 million of this increase will occur in North America, Europe, the Soviet Union, and Oceania, i.e., the parts of the world which are now developed and well-fed. The fifteen-year increase in Asia, Africa, and Latin America will more than equal the total population of the developed countries today.

Based on the trends of agricultural development of the past five years, it is my belief that Asia, Africa, and Latin America will not be able to feed one billion more people by 1980, even at the present low levels of nutrition, to say nothing of providing them with clothing, housing, education, transportation, and the other minimal amenities of modern life.

While the populations of Asia, Africa, and Latin America have been increasing steadily and rapidly, food production in these continents has not been keeping up with the population growth, particularly during the past eight years since 1960. During the decade 1950 to 1960 food production in all three of the underdeveloped continents made fairly good progress, running somewhat ahead of the population growth. But since 1960 there has been an ominous slowing down in food production while the populations have continued to increase at an even faster pace.

Without going into detailed statistics, the general picture is that since 1960 food production in Asia, Africa, and Latin America has been growing at rates of 1 per cent to 2 per cent per year while populations have been growing at rates of 2 per cent to 4 per cent per year, leaving a gap of over 1 per cent per year. The disparity varies a great deal among the ninety countries of Asia, Africa, and Latin America. The disparity between food production and population growth has been particularly acute in Latin America where food production per capita on the average has declined nearly 10 per cent since 1960. The disparity is somewhat less for Asia and Africa, but it is a serious problem in all three continents.

If these trends continue for the next ten to fifteen years, mass starvation will inevitably result, and this would be famine on a scale never before experienced in the world's history. There have been many famines in history involving millions of people, but none involving hundreds of millions of people. Not only will such famines be widespread, but they will be persistent and probably get worse year by year. It is hard for us sitting in rich, comfortable, overfed America to realize that the greatest disaster in the history of the world is just around the corner.

All these problems resulting from large increases in population can be solved by science, political action, and money. Food production can be increased, water and air pollution can be reduced, urban deterioration can be corrected, and hopefully even the social problems can be improved—through the application of science implemented by political action and money. But all these things take time. They can't be done overnight or in a few months or even in a few years. *Time is the crucial factor.* And time is what the world does not have.

As a result of the rapidly increasing populations in Asia, Africa, and Latin America—and also in the United States—these technical and social problems are developing and multiplying faster than they can be solved. Many billions of dollars will be poured into trying to solve these problems in the next decade, but they will not be solved unless the rate of population growth can be reduced. In fact, the problems may get worse in spite of the billions of dollars put into trying to solve them.

This is where birth control comes into the picture as the only hope of preserving social and political stability on this planet. Lower birth rates are needed in most of the world in order to give science and society time to solve these multiplying problems. Neither science nor politics nor money nor religion, powerful forces as they are, can solve these problems unless there is time.

In fact, it may already be too late for birth control to have any real impact on the impending world food/population problem which seems likely to reach crisis proportions within the next ten years. Only a really massive application of birth control in most of the countries of Asia, Africa, and Latin America within the next few years could have a major effect in reducing the severity of the impending food/population crisis of the 1970s.

India is undoubtedly the most vulnerable country in the world today. India's population in 1965 was nearly 500 million—more than North and South America put together—and India will increase her population by at least 200 million more people in the next fifteen years if present birth rates continue. In my opinion, India cannot possibly feed 200 million more people by 1980, even at the appallingly low nutritional level now prevalent in India. India could feed 200 million more people by 2000, maybe even by 1990, but not by 1980. There are many reasons for this, too complex to review in this paper.

The United States is now sending more than a billion dollars' worth of food to India per year and that is all that is keeping India from starvation today. We will have to send much more in the next few years. And there are many other countries which are almost as close to starvation as India. But the great American food surplus is nearing an end. The population of the United States is increasing at over three million per year, and the increasing demands of our own population plus commercial exports will reduce our food surplus to zero in only a few more years under existing agricultural policies. We will soon have to make every effort to increase U.S. agricultural production to a maximum. It is fortunate that we have this possibility, although the potential for increased production is limited. Again we need time.

In the long run birth control is the only answer. Death rates will continue to decline in all countries, unless mass starvation or large-scale war intervenes. Therefore birth rates all over the world must decline or these problems will continue to get larger and more insoluble. As far as food supply is concerned, I put 1990 as the outside date at which mass starvation can be avoided in Asia and Latin America even by the most optimistic improvement in agriculture, if present birth rates continue. And this could be extremely optimistic. Pope Paul's statement on this subject to the United Nations on October 4, 1965, was, in my opinion, ill-advised and based on misinformation. Pope Paul's advisers obviously do not understand the facts of world agriculture and the limited possibilities for rapid increases in agricultural production in the less developed countries.

Unfortunately, it seems unlikely that birth control can have a major impact on birth rates in Asia, Africa, and Latin America before the 1980s. And these continents will probably be in the grip of widespread starvation before then. Nevertheless, the sooner the vulnerable countries get started on serious programs to reduce their birth rates, the better. The world food shortage in the 1970s may be disastrous, but in the 1980s it may be catastrophic.

This is a world-wide problem, and therefore I suggest that all countries in the world, with only a few exceptions, should take steps to reduce their birth rates below twenty per thousand and their population growth rates below 1 per cent per year. Most of the countries of Europe and also Japan already have done this, principally through the application of contraception and abortion as methods of birth control. The United States needs to reduce its population growth rate below the present rate of 1.7 per cent per year because we are literally running out of good-quality living space.

Most of the countries of Asia, Africa, and Latin America now have population growth rates of 2 per cent to 4 per cent per year, and these rates must be reduced because their primitive agricultures and low levels of education cannot keep up with such high population growth rates. Only a few countries such as the Soviet Union, Canada, Australia, Argentina, and South Africa have the resources to continue to tolerate population growth rates over 1 per cent per year for more than a few more years.

My conclusion therefore is that the quality of life will decline in most of the countries of the world unless birth rates are reduced—and this includes the United States. In the more vulnerable countries, continuing high birth rates will cause increasing poverty, mass starvation, and political instability in the next ten to fifteen years. Birth control is the only answer.

7

OUR EXPERIENCE WITH RHYTHM

by Dr. and Mrs. André J. de Bethune

Dr. de Bethune took his Ph.D. degree in physical chemistry at Columbia University and did war research on the Manhattan project under Nobel prize-winner Professor Harold C. Urey. He has been a National Research fellow at the Massachusetts Institute of Technology and a Guggenheim fellow at Yale. He is a professor of chemistry and acting chairman of the chemistry department at Boston College.

Born on August 8, 1927, in New York City, Mrs. de Bethune studied at St. John's University in Brooklyn and at Grailville Community College, Loveland, Ohio.

The testimony of Dr. and Mrs. de Bethune was presented on March 2, 1966, at the hearings before the Subcommittee on Foreign Aid Expenditure of the Committee on Government Operations, United States Senate, 89th Congress, 2nd session on Senate Bill 1676. This is a bill to reorganize the Department of State and the Department of Health, Education, and Welfare.

Today I wish to speak only as a private citizen and as the father of a family. A year ago, President Lyndon Johnson, in his State of the Union Message to Congress and to the people said: "I will seek new ways to use our knowledge to help deal with the explosion in world population." Pope John XXIII addressed the same problem in his encyclical letter "Mater et Magistra" when he showed his concern over the "aucta cumulatus hominum multitudo"—the ever-increasing multitude of men piling up.

Today, my wife, Margaret, here present, and I propose to speak to you about our experience with the population explosion at home. My wife and I were married in June 1949, according to the rites of the Roman Catholic Church. We were well acquainted with our Church's disapproval of artificial birth control on moral grounds, but we also knew that our Church permitted child spacing via the rhythm method. Our first experience of child spacing via rhythm began after the birth of our first child, a girl, in September 1950. Our first attempts were made by the calendar method.

This resulted in two more children, a second girl and a boy, within the next thirty-six months, after spacings of fourteen and twenty-two months, respectively. These spacings included periods of five months and thirteen months, respectively, of total abstinence or rhythm divorce. We computed Ogino rhythm calendars with wide safety margins, calling for two full weeks, and three full weeks, respectively, of abstinence in cycles of thirty to thirty-five days in length. In both cases, *the rhythm method failed in the very first month of its application,* evidence that my wife had had each time a late ovulation.

After our third child, our obstetrician put us on the thermometer, without, however, guaranteeing any results. The temperature method of rhythm is based on the daily morning observation of a woman's temperature, at the moment of awakening, before rising—this is known as the basal body temperature or BBT. An ordinary fever thermometer may be used; many people prefer a special BBT thermometer with an expanded scale in the interval from 95° to 100° Fahrenheit. Special BBT thermometers could not be sold in the state of Connecticut under that state's recently invalidated birth control laws—courses of instruction in the use of BBT are still illegal in Massachusetts under the birth control laws of the Commonwealth.

A woman's basal body temperature normally shows a small but definite temperature rise of about one half to three quarters of a degree

Fahrenheit at ovulation, and an equal temperature drop at menstruation. Thus, in principle, the temperature chart gives the timing of ovulation. In practice, there are many difficulties and pitfalls—false rises, multiple rises—which obscure the chart and make it difficult to interpret.

With, or despite, the help of the thermometer as a child-spacing device, we were to have six more children during the next ninety-nine months: a second boy after seventeen months, a third girl after sixteen months, a third boy after sixteen months, a fourth girl after sixteen months, a fifth girl after seventeen months, and a fourth boy, our ninth child, after seventeen months. The difficulties we had with the thermometer are best illustrated by the last of this group of cycles. In this cycle, we entered rhythm divorce on the seventh day, the day after cessation of menstrual bleeding. The temperature rose about two thirds of a degree Fahrenheit on the sixteenth day, dropped, and recovered from the nineteenth through the twenty-second day going up to its normal high level.

We then broke the rhythm divorce. The temperature then unexpectedly dropped about one third of a degree Fahrenheit until the thirty-third day, when it rose again to its previous high level, and stayed high, and my wife was pregnant. Here is an instance of an ovulation which occurred, as proved by pregnancy, some twelve to fourteen days later than the timing deduced from the temperature chart. My wife's cumulative pregnancy rate, from the birth of our first to the birth of our ninth child, was eight pregnancies in 11¼ years for a pregnancy rate of seventy-one per hundred woman-years total time. The normal pregnancy rate is 100, or one child per year, for a fertile population that practices no family limitation. A medically acceptable method of family limitation should have a pregnancy rate no higher than ten per hundred woman-years.

Our ninth child is now four years and two months old. If we have had no more children since, it is no thanks to the rhythm method. I would like to put into the record the type of cycles my wife has been experiencing since the birth of our baby in December 1961. There was first a period of 104 days of amenorrhea; this was followed by a cycle of eighty-three days in which ovulation, as detected by BBT, occurred on the eightieth day; then a cycle of thirty-nine days; then a cycle of nineteen days with ovulation on the eleventh day; then a cycle of thirty-six days with ovulation on the twenty-ninth day; then a cycle of forty-three days with ovulation on the thirty-sixth day.

This was followed by a cycle of twenty-eight days with ovulation on the twenty-first day; then a cycle of forty-one days with ovulation on the thirty-second day; then a cycle of thirty-two days with ovulation on the twenty-eighth day; then a cycle of thirty-six days with ovulation on the thirty-first day; then a cycle of forty-four days with ovulation on the thirty-second day; then a cycle of thirty-four days with ovulation on the twenty-eighth day; then a cycle of seventy-four days with ovulation on the sixty-fifth day; then a cycle of thirty-four days with ovulation on the twenty-fourth day; then a cycle of forty-five days which was anovulatory; then a cycle of twenty days with ovulation on the seventeenth day; then a cycle of fifty-two days with ovulation on the forty-eighth day; then a cycle of thirty-four days with ovulation on the twenty-fourth day; then a cycle of forty-eight days with ovulation on the 42nd day; then a cycle of forty-six days with ovulation on the thirty-seventh day.

This was followed by a cycle of thirty-two days which was anovulatory; then a cycle of twenty days with ovulation on the sixteenth day; then a cycle of forty-three days which was anovulatory; then a cycle of thirty-eight days which was anovulatory; then a cycle of forty days with ovulation on either the twenty-ninth or the thirty-sixth day; then a cycle of thirty-three days with ovulation on the thirtieth day; then a cycle of forty-three days with ovulation not recorded; then a cycle of thirty-two days with ovulation not recorded; then a cycle of thirty-six days with ovulation not recorded; then a cycle of fifty days with ovulation on the thirty-third day; then a cycle of forty-nine days with ovulation not recorded; then a cycle of thirty-eight days with

ovulation not recorded; then a cycle of thirty days with ovulation not recorded; then a cycle of fifty-three days with ovulation on the forty-fourth day; then a cycle of fifty-three days with ovulation on the thirty-first day; then a cycle of thirty-four days with ovulation on the twenty-sixth day.

It is clear from the record presented to you that rhythm—calendar or BBT—is completely impracticable for my wife and for me. The advice that we use the rhythm method to regulate the further growth of our family must be considered either a bad joke or a display of invincible ignorance. The etiology of our recent infertility remains obscure. It is only this year that my wife has found time, at the urging of friends and at my urging, to undertake a long-needed course of gynecological treatment.

In bringing this personal tale to a close, I would like to base my further reflections on certain authentic, but little known and poorly understood, statements of the popes. Pope Paul VI has repeatedly let it be known that he is waiting for his papal population commission to reach a workable consensus before he can "feel obliged in conscience to change" previous papal norms. It is my belief that these existing papal norms can be used to justify much more extensive research and development in family planning than has usually been thought to be the case. Let me show you how.

In his address of October 29, 1951, to the Italian Union of Obstetrical Nurses, Pope Pius XII said: "To spouses, who make use of the specific act of the marriage state, nature and the Creator enjoin the function of providing for the preservation of mankind. This is the 'gift of children' which gives to their state its proper value. From the positive obligation of procreation, married couples may be exempted, for a long time, or even for the whole marriage, by serious motives such as those often found in the medical, eugenic, economic and social 'indication.'"

On November 26, 1951, Pope Pius XII spoke to the Italian Family Front. Here he said: "The primary office of marriage is to be at the service of life. But the Church can consider with sympathy and comprehension the real difficulties of married life in our own day. We have affirmed the legitimacy and the truly broad limits of a regulation of births, which, unlike so-called 'birth control,' is compatible with the law of God. One may even hope that medical science will succeed in giving to this licit method of sufficiently secure foundation, and the most recent information seems to confirm such a hope."

In this address to the Italian Family Front, Pope Pius XII coined the expression "the regulation of births" to emphasize the moral legitimacy of intentional family limitation and to distinguish it from so-called "birth control," as condemned by the Roman Catholic Church.

Wherein does the distinction between the two lie? To establish this distinction, Pope Pius XII went back to the writings of his predecessor, Pope Pius XI, in his encyclical letter of 1930 on marriage.

In this encyclical, Pope Pius XI had condemned birth control "by human industry," but did approve of conjugal relations "conducted in a rightful and natural manner, even though a new life cannot spring forth because of natural causes." Later on, in his address of October 29, 1951, already alluded to, Pope Pius XII expressed his approval of "the observance of times of infecundity." In his address of September 12, 1958, Pope Pius XII approved of "the taking advantage of natural temporary sterility."

There is nothing in these papal words that restricts these principles to the female sex. Yet for the past thirty-six years, studies on the natural methods of family limitation have been concentrating almost exclusively on the regular or irregular rhythmic cycle of fertility and sterility of woman. The "taking advantage of natural temporary sterility," to use Pope Pius XII's own expression, in the male sex is equally valid in the light of the papal principles . . . .

I should like to close with three brief quotations. The first is from the address of Leon Joseph Cardinal Suenens, archbishop of Brussels and Malines, to the World Catholic Health Congress, held in Brussels in 1958. Cardinal Suenens was then bishop and professor of moral theology at the Catholic University of Louvain. He said: "We cannot ask men to respect a law, without doing all in our power to make obedience possible, without teaming up all our energies to open up new ways." I would like to bring out the parallelism between Cardinal Suenens' statement and President Johnson's. Both the cardinal and the President called for *new ways* of dealing with this problem.

The second is from the Vatican Council II's constitution on *The Church in the Modern World,* promulgated by Pope Paul VI in December 1965: "Those skilled in biological, medical, social, and psychological sciences can contribute greatly to the good of marriage and of the family and to the peace of consciences if, by pooling their studies, they strive to elucidate the conditions favorable to an honest ordering of human procreation."

The third is from Pope Paul VI's address of March 27, 1965, to the Special Papal Commission on Population Problems: "The Church at all times has been concerned to give adequate answers to the great problems facing men. For this purpose, and according to the advice of the Lord, the Church welcomes 'things new and old' (Matthew 13:52). While very difficult problems are raised, is there not also the heralding of solutions for problems which seem today so difficult to solve? We want to believe and hope so."

These purposes, as expressed by Cardinal Suenens, by Vatican Council II, by Pope Paul VI, as well as by President Johnson, can well be subserved by Senator Gruening's bill calling for the creation of Offices of Population Problems in the Department of State, and in the Department of Health, Education, and Welfare, and for the holding of a White House Conference on Population Problems. Therefore, as an individual citizen of the United States and of the Commonwealth of Massachusetts, as an individual Catholic, and as the father of nine children, I wish to express my wholehearted support for Senate Bill 1676.

Senator Gruening. Well, thank you very much, Dr. de Bethune. You have made a very real contribution to this discussion. May we conclude from your very detailed and careful testimony that the rhythm method so far as Mrs. de Bethune and you are concerned was a failure?

Dr. de Bethune. In our own personal experience, as an individual family, it was a failure.

Senator Gruening. Would you make any general deduction from that as to its fallibility or nonfallibility in general? Would you say that your experience was unusual, exceptional or not?

Dr. de Bethune. I would like to qualify my answer under two headings, Senator. We know many other families whose experiences have paralleled ours. We know some families where—one family, specifically, of six children—where the husband and wife finally decided to live a life of what I would call divorce within the same house, and this has been going on for four or five years now. They cannot trust the rhythm method and they feel in conscience they can do nothing else. This is by no means uncommon. . . .

Senator Gruening. I would like to make this observation in your case and the case of those people you know. You are people of intelligence, education, and clearly with a firm determination.based on your religious belief to make this rhythm method work. Is it fair to conclude that in the case of people with less education, less restraint, the probabilities of failure would be even greater, particularly in the slums, the favelas and barriadas to which Dr. Barrett referred, where people do not have the opportunity to watch the calendar or take these regular observations. Would not the probability of failure be infinitely greater?

Dr. de Bethune. I would answer affirmatively. I think the whole problem of family limitation, regardless of the methods, hinges upon motivation, and motivation in the case of rhythm must be extremely strong if any success is to be achieved.

Senator Gruening. Does not this divorce within the same home to which you alluded impose a great deal of hardship and distress and deprivation on the part of those people? It is a great tribute to the quality of their faith that they are willing to undergo that.

Dr. de Bethune. I would answer affirmatively—it does cause a great deal of hardship. I do not want to get emotional about it. I will just say yes.

Senator Gruening. Mrs. de Bethune, we would be very happy to hear from you.

Testimony of Mrs. André J. de Bethune

Senator Gruening, it is very nice of you to listen to me because I am not an expert, but I have some very definite views about these things. And I would like to say about this particular case you are referring to: It is a sin against the marriage to live in this way, it brings disintegration within the family for this to go on. I mean, self-restraint may be good but it is not the nature of marriage to be this way. And tensions are created in such a way that, I think, it cripples the family to some degree. I would never really recommend a prolonged length of abstinence for anyone.

I would like to make four main points here, and some of them are very short.

First, information on methods of family limitations should be freely and readily available to married couples, as they may need this information, and as they feel they can conscientiously make use of it. This is particularly needed by the underprivileged members of our society, who may not be able to afford the services of a private physician.

Second, the purpose of Senate Bill 1676 should be clarified to make it clear that the proposed Offices of Population Problems will promote the well-being of the family, as a social unit, as well as the need for family limitation. What I am saying is that the right to bear and rear children is a fundamental, basic, natural, human right for a married couple, and that this right should always be safeguarded and protected and that no legal stigma should ever attach to the having of children. This is a point of fundamental importance on which the purposes of the bill, as they stand, need to be made clearer.

Third, the right to have and to bear children needs to be safeguarded especially for underprivileged families, together with their right to free access to information on family limitation. Families in less favored circumstances should not be pressured by the full weight and prestige of the government into not having the children that a married couple would normally and naturally desire. They should also be free from any official pressure, or express or implied coercion, to limit their families in a manner that violates their own conscientious beliefs. The purposes of the bill need to be clarified on this point.

Fourth, the temperature—BBT—method of rhythm, as described by my husband, can become potentially a source of great benefit to families, as a means of growth in self-knowledge and mutual love by husbands and wives. In our case, the method did not succeed as a child-spacing device, but it has still proved invaluable as a source of information much appreciated by my gynecologist. . . .

I would also like to say—and I am going to stick my neck out on this, and, at this point, I really do not care, I think it needs to be said —as far as the Catholic Church is concerned, I know the teaching of the Church in regard to artificial means of birth control. I am not speaking here of attacks on a life already started, on abortion, or on mutilation of the body by sterilization, but as far as the usual means of contraceptive devices, these practices are considered to be serious sins in the eyes of the Church. It is my firm belief that if you want to teach people how to be good and integrated, you cannot beat them morally in this way because they are looking for something good.

I believe that every man and wife when they marry want the goodness of society through their children. And I believe that the Church —maybe we will never be able to reach a common denominator for this—I believe that if the Church could regard these artificial methods of birth control as a less perfect means of achieving good rather than a sin, which is an awful load on the conscience of so many people, if they could regard it as a less perfect means progressing toward the more perfect and integrating means, they would perhaps begin to talk to the souls of people. And I believe that is all I have to say and I must thank you again for listening to me.

Senator Gruening. Well, thank you very much, Dr. and Mrs. de Bethune, for a very moving presentation and a very vital one. I do not think that I could add anything by any comments I might make. You have made a very important contribution to this problem. Thank you very much.

8

FAMILY PLANNING

by Joseph M. Krebs

Dr. Krebs is associate professor of gynecology and obstetrics at St. Louis University Medical School. He has addressed the Missouri State Medical Association on family planning.

Attempts to deal with the fecundity of the human being are as ancient as history itself. The recognition of the cyclic nature of fertility in the female is itself also ancient. In Genesis 18, Abraham and Sarah are extending hospitality to two strangers, one of whom proves to be Yahweh. This guest states, "I shall visit you again next year without fail, and your wife will then have a son." The text goes on to say, "Now Abraham and Sarah were old, well on in years, and Sarah had ceased to have her monthly periods. So Sarah laughed to herself thinking, 'Now that I am past the age of childbearing, my husband is an old man, is pleasure to come my way again?'"

St. Augustine castigates the Manichaeans of his day as doing grave wrong by utilizing their imperfect conception of a "safe time," because of his idea that sexual intercourse without the possibility of procreation was very wrong. He felt the only excuse for this relationship between man and woman was reproduction of the species.

In the book *The Infertile Period,* a classic in reproduction physiology as it was known up to 1962, Hartman states that investigators in Germany and France discovered in the 1840s that female dogs, which have a bloodstained vaginal discharge when they are in heat, ovulate toward the end of this period. Since women also bleed periodically, he points out, it was natural to assume, in the absence of data to the contrary, that they must also ovulate at the time of bleeding.

The modern basis for our more correct understanding of the limited fertility of the female was reasoned independently by two observers separated by a vast number of miles across the earth. Ogino in Japan and Knaus in Germany in the 1930s determined the time of ovulation to be within a certain time period which could be sometimes ascertained by thorough study of the menstrual pattern. Since their scientific breakthrough, little additional *significant* information has been forthcoming, although many efforts to improve the pinpointing of this phenomenon have been attempted.

The crux of successful practice of periodic continence is the precise knowledge of when the woman ovulates. John Rock admonishes, because so many failed to consider, "that the time of ovulation is no way effected, much less determined, by a preceding menstruation, which of itself has nothing to do with ovulation."

Unfortunately we cannot *predict* this transient episode of monumental import with any degree of accuracy. For practical purposes, our recognition of the event even after it has taken place is proved scientifically only by the occurrence of a pregnancy. Ovulation has been observed in the human but it is, of course, impractical at the present time to observe this with each cycle.

We are dependent today on the recognition of many probable signs of ovulation. Some of these are better than others and some have received wide acceptance. All of them add up to only a degree of reasonableness which falls short of certainty. Because of this, rhythm or periodic continence remains an unpredictable and unreliable and altogether vexatious answer to the struggling couple confronted with the need for fertility control. Often the very anxiety state which results from the precipitating factor, plus the realization of previous failures, makes the hypothalamic control of ovulation even more uncertain.

Despite the limitation of family planning by traditional Catholic teachings to this device; despite the fact that Pius XII exhorted scientists to make "this licit method" more reliable to those who need it; despite the fact that there are five Catholic medical schools in this country, not one of these has published the results of any research which would throw light on this tormenting problem. There has been a paucity of Catholic publication in scientific journals to really evaluate periodic continence in its reliability for couples restricted to its use.

Reports by others found in the literature indicate that rhythm is approximately comparable to the effectiveness of the various mechanical methods. All are familiar with the lack of protection offered by these means on occasion.

And yet there are many popular articles by enthusiastic members of the laity, professional medics, and clerics which intimate that rhythm is a successful alternative to means which are considered of dubious morality at present. The experience of most couples practicing periodic abstinence is that it is very difficult, not at all consistent with their natural rhythms for expressing mutual love, and, worst of all, unreliable.

Prior to the middle of this century, regulation of conception was feared to be a form of hedonism. The main factor causing the Church to review her concept of conjugal morality seems to be the hard fact of population density. There has also been a recognition in medical disciplines that pregnancy is not exactly a normal state of the female.

She is known to at least experience an altered physiological response during this time. Certain disease processes in the female are recognized by conscientious practitioners as contraindications to further pregnancies. The dependence on such an uncertain means as capricious as rhythm is inconsistent with reason. The alternative of total abstinence, as the only means of conception control, is without compassion. Heroic practices are always to be admired. Are they to be demanded?

It is recognized that *all* couples practice periodic continence from sexual relations from time to time, even those whose moral consciences permit absolute contraception. In times of fatigue, illness, absence from the partner, these episodes of abstinence are accepted without question. Periodic continence, too, can be practiced by many, particularly those willing to make sacrifices for their own and mutual betterment. But to be surprised by a pregnancy after resolute periodic continence is unacceptable to most Catholic couples. It is particularly cruel on the part of many medics and clerics to intimate that this pregnancy would not have occurred if this couple had only followed the rules.

Many couples stanchly and honestly maintain that rhythm works for them, and they fail to understand their friends who speak of failures. While these couples are successfully enjoying their relationship, it is probably due to their sexuality, mutually agreed upon, with relations two or three times a month. Such couples probably would never need rhythm to limit their family size; this degree of sexual exposure is known to result in low fecundity.

Not all or even most couples can restrict their mutual giving of one another to this degree of frequency. Most doctors are well aware of some family situations where this exposure rate is forced by one partner on another. The Church has always opposed such restrictions unless by mutual consent.

Periodic continence will be successful in postponing, for a greater or lesser period of time, a pregnancy in couples who are motivated to studying very carefully the menstrual cycle, in all of the parameters known today, and who are willing to make sacrfices and restrict their natural expression of conjugal love. Periodic continence will not offer any degree of certainty to those women who have a more urgent or definite need for having no more pregnancies.

If periodic continence were more reliable, there seems to be little doubt that it would be one of the most widely used methods in the world. Many people would be able and willing to refrain from relations for a reasonable period of time. Considering the vagaries of human ovulation, as we know it today, the hopes for such reliability are not foreseeable in the near future.

Practically all of the mechanical, chemical, and medicinal methods of conception control, albeit more reliable, have their disadvantages in aesthetics, anxiety over side effects, complications, and consequences.

Many considerations are used in judging available methods of conception control. These will include, among others, patient acceptance, ease of employment, moral connotations, and degree of protection inherent in the method. If this latter criterion is the one of greatest concern, then oral ovulatory suppression is the first choice.

This is not to say that the anovulants represent a panacea for all the world's problems with overpopulation. Fertility control per se will not automatically feed or clothe or adequately house the great masses of underprivileged throughout the world. The use of anovulants still requires a degree of mental concentration which is difficult to follow by many of these unfortunates.

However, when the consequences of the anovulants are not feared by the patient or her husband, and when she is reasonably motivated to follow relatively simple instructions, she is rewarded with practically 100 per cent effectiveness. The evolution of newer pills has greatly reduced the incidence of side effects. Still many patients and/or their husbands remain concerned by all the articles appearing in communications media which speak of the uncertainty of consequences and side effects.

This anxiety is strange in view of the widespread usage of these agents. Such acceptable medicaments as aspirin, penicillin, and others are widely accepted without reservations, despite the knowledge they have indeed caused mortality as well as morbidity.

Most side effects of the anovulants are well known and are usually accepted by the patients; few have been found to be serious. In the women in whom pregnancy itself would cause hormonologic damage, the pill is very apt to mimic this problem, usually though to a less serious degree. Diabetes is said to be such an example and should be watched for. It is, of course, easier to stop the pill than the pregnancy it is given to forestall. The consequences of the pregnancy must in each instance be weighed against the consequences of the pill. . . .

Family planning is now established as an aspect of medical practice that has assumed its place of importance because of the needs of patients. Catholics are likewise interested in limiting their fertility potential. They hope to do this in accordance with moral principles. The preoccupation with the fear of hedonism that prevented theologians from understanding the true conjugal relationship is now fortunately on the wane. The laity must become more articulate in expressing what the marital relationship means. Together with professionals, the laity must help to form a conceptualization of what the vocation of marriage really signifies.

The papal commission formed by good Pope John and continued and enlarged by the present Pontiff is testimony of the desire of the magisterium to review attitudes held for centuries but based on biology poorly understood.

If Catholics are to be limited to the practice of periodic continence, as we now know it or can expect it to work in the foreseeable future, little control of fertility can be expected. The anovulant pill, despite a great deal of debate regarding side effects and potential dangers of prolonged usage, has enjoyed general acceptance by patients and doctors alike.

9

TOWARD A WORLD OF WANTED CHILDREN

by Lois Mattox Miller

Lois Mattox Miller has written many articles for *Reader's Digest* that have attracted wide attention. She is at present one of the roving editors for the *Digest*.

In April 1967 the elegant, century-old Teatro Municipal in Santiago, Chile, was the scene of an international conference that smashed many Old World traditions and swept aside ancient religious and political taboos. For the first time, the capital of a predominantly (95 per cent) Roman Catholic country became the platform for open discussion of such formerly forbidden subjects as abortion, contraception, birth control, and—most importantly—of "planned parenthood" as the only sure means of stemming the world's avalanche of unwanted babies.

Despite the unusual setting, the world conference of the International Planned Parenthood Federation (IPPF) was marked by great good will. President Eduardo Frei Montalva greeted the fifteen hundred delegates from eighty-seven nations, and for a whole week Santiago made headlines around the world. On the evening of April 12, for example, a "near riot" took place when two thousand teen-agers clamored for admission to the auditorium's jammed galleries. However, these were serious, well-behaved boys and girls, many of whom had traveled far to attend an IPPF session devoted to "Youth and Sex." "We are hungry for reliable information about sex," one young girl explained. "We don't get it from our parents or our teachers." But they must have an intelligent understanding of it if they are to become good wives and mothers.

The individual's right to plan and limit the family's size was proclaimed by the conference to be a basic human right, and the delegates approved unanimously the call for concentrated action by the United Nations on family planning made by the keynote speaker, Lord Caradon, British Minister of State and Representative to the United Nations. (For the first time all the UN agencies were represented officially at an IPPF conference.) "I can imagine no better way," Lord Caradon said, "of making Human Rights Year (1968) a blessing to mankind."

Other highlights from Santiago:

Governments representing three quarters of the world's people have initiated or approved family-planning programs directed at the poor and illiterate populations that need help most.

Laws in various countries prohibiting dissemination of contraceptive information are being modified or annulled. Effective and safe contraception is generally accepted as the only solution to the world-wide problem of abortion—now "the greatest epidemic of all time."

Roman Catholic priests, doctors, and educators were among the official representatives to the conference. And priests from six Latin-American countries signed a declaration that "perfection in marriage demands that certain means be taken to plan one's family responsibly" and that "whatever means are considered medically viable be used to achieve perfection."

Surveys made in more than a dozen countries revealed that from 60 to 80 per cent of the people who had heard of family planning for the first time welcomed—and demanded—information. The reasons generally given: "concern for a better standard of living and a better chance in life for children."

Veterans of the planned-parenthood movement found these advances breath-taking. One man active in the crusade for decades said, "I never expected to see this day." The remark was overheard by a Latin-

American monsignor who added, "Nor did I, *señor*. We must be grateful for the wisdom of God."

One regret dampened the spirits of the Santiago meeting: Margaret Sanger, the "Mother of Planned Parenthood," had died in 1966 at the age of eighty-two. Had she lived another seven months she could have witnessed in the IPPF conference the all but universal acknowledgement of the ideal to which she had devoted a lifetime. "Margaret Sanger," said Dr. Alan F. Guttmacher, outstanding medical authority on human fertility, "was a pioneer not only in democratizing birth control, but also in contraceptive methodology. She championed the idea that contraception is not a simple function of kitchen medicine; like any other medical therapy, it should be under the control of physicians."

As a young visiting nurse working in 1912 on New York's Lower East Side, Margaret Sanger was appalled by the many unhealthy and impoverished mothers whom she saw burdened by unwanted pregnancies, and by the birth of so many unwanted children into already large families. She appealed to doctors for help, and was informed that nothing could be done—dissemination of information on contraception was illegal under a federal law enacted in 1873.

In Europe the situation was somewhat different, however, and in 1915 Margaret Sanger traveled to Amsterdam, where the Dutch physician, Dr. Aletta Jacobs, had pioneered in teaching contraception in clinics, and Dr. Johannes Rutgers had set up the world's first real birth-control clinic. There she observed Dr. Rutgers quietly teaching contraceptive techniques to Dutch mothers, making examinations and prescribing the method most suitable to each case, and working under dignified and aseptic clinical conditions.

Inspired by what she saw there, Mrs. Sanger opened the first American birth-control clinic in New York in 1916. For the rest of her life she campaigned for the right to give contraceptive information to the people. Gradually the barriers came down—and today new and better methods are available.

Wherever the topic of contraception is introduced nowadays the main questions seem to be: Which contraceptive? What method? How effective is it—and how safe? Throughout the free world, planned parenthood is a voluntary act of the individual. In clinics, principles of all methods are explained and the woman makes her own choice, with expert advice.

IPPF itself prefers, in order of effectiveness: 1. oral contraceptives (since 1966 the preference of about 71 per cent of women in U.S. Planned Parenthood clinics), 2. the intrauterine devices, and 3. the diaphragm, preferably in combination with spermicidal jellies or creams. The rhythm method is taught for Catholic clients, although planned-parenthood authorities deplore rhythm's high rate of failure. Dr. John Rock, a Catholic physician who is responsible for much of the clinical work with oral contraceptives, says that the basic trouble is that "ovulation in many women is not rhythmic."

As seen from the Santiago conference, the advance of the planned-parenthood movement has been widely accepted in the United States, Britain, the Scandinavian countries (notably Sweden), the Netherlands, and Japan. The idea has also taken root in the emerging nations of Africa and Asia.

Family planning faces its big challenge in Latin America, which has the world's highest birth rate. Its population is growing 2.8 per cent annually, compared to 2.5 per cent in Asia and 1.5 per cent in North America. Unless this birth rate is curbed, the continent's population (253 million at present) will more than double in the next twenty-five years.

Ironically, two decades of social and economic development seem only to have compounded the problem. Health programs, mass immunization, and modern sanitation methods have dramatically reduced death rates, but nothing has been done to curb the Latin family's tendency to multiply. "The population problem was side-stepped," says Dr. Alberto Lleras Camargo, former President of Colombia. "Nobody sounded the warning in time, and all of us—clergymen and military, politicians and sociologists—have been caught by surprise."

Now the booming birth rate threatens to block the Alliance for Progress and frustrate popular hopes inspired by the "revolution of rising expectations." People are flocking from the rural areas to the already overcrowded cities, and Latin America has been *forced* at last to face the necessity of population control. Contraception and family planning are now discussed openly, with facts *and* facilities being brought directly to people on the lowest social and economic levels.

Family-planning clinics operate in every country except Bolivia. Mexico and Uruguay permit private planned-parenthood groups to operate in public hospitals and health clinics. Colombia and El Salvador also provide training in contraceptive methods to public-health doctors, nurses, midwives, and other medical workers.

Chile has the most advanced program in Latin America, officially sponsored by the National Health Service. (Costa Rica and Honduras also provide contraception as part of government health programs.) There are birth-control clinics in every public hospital in Santiago and in many provinces, as well as in numerous private institutions. "They are ordinarily filled to capacity," says Dr. Hernan Romero, professor of preventive and social medicine at the University of Chile. "The Chilean woman has learned from experience that she needn't bear three children to keep one, and that too many offspring can become a truly agonizing burden."

Like many another Latin-American country, Chile's active interest in family planning grew out of the problem of widespread abortions. Dr. Romero reports that abortion is induced in one out of every two or three cases of pregnancy and that such cases tie up 20 per cent of the beds in maternity and gynecology wards. Last year, abortion was responsible for two out of every five obstetric deaths, and the ratio was nearer three out of five in urban areas.

Surveys conducted in eight Latin-American capitals by the UN Latin-American Demographic Center in Santiago reveal generally a "favorable attitude toward family planning in a large segment of the population concerned." But public opinion on this delicate question is difficult to determine. Women are reluctant to express views for fear of revealing personal practice. So the most reliable information may come from doctors. Says Dr. Romero: "Doctors report almost unanimously that religious or moral objections are exceptional. The majority of women, about 75 per cent, feel that birth control should be made universal and that the Church has no right to interfere."

The Roman Catholic Church in Latin America no longer represents a formidable barrier to planned parenthood. Opposition has been replaced by intelligent, if cautious, co-operation. "The Catholic church favors the idea of family planning in Latin America," says Dr. Ramiro Delgado Garcia of Colombia, "provided the methods used are 'natural' and the aim is regulation of family size within the general context of responsible parenthood."

In Europe opposition to family planning is strongest in the Irish Republic, where birth control, except by the rhythm method, is illegal and the law is strictly enforced. Spain strictly forbids "initiating means to inhibit procreation." Italy suffers from the consequences of harsh anticontraceptive decrees passed by the Fascist regime in 1930. The laws are still in effect, but a parliamentary group is studying possible modifications or repeal.

Last July, France's National Assembly voted to repeal its strict 1920 law, which banned all contraceptives, as well as birth-control propaganda. Intended to raise the birth rate to replenish population losses in World War I, the law was never strictly enforced and contraceptives of most types have been available, with the exception of diaphragms (which could be ordered from abroad). There is also a strong family-planning organization, founded in 1956, which has more than a hundred centers throughout France.

Canada, however, is the world's outstanding example of how a modern, progressive nation has lived with an archaic and unenforceable law and has, despite it, achieved a stable population, a low birth rate, and an enlightened attitude toward contraception. The Canadian Criminal Code specifies: "Everyone commits an offense who offers to sell, advertises or has for sale any means, instructions, medicine, drug or article intended as a method of preventing conception . . . ."

Nevertheless, Canadians have manifested a strong preference for determining the size of their own families. The birth rate dropped to a record low of 19.4 in 1966.[1] The Canadian Gallup polls reveal an increasing number of Canadians favoring contraception: 48 per cent in 1952, 55 per cent in 1961 and 67 per cent in 1965. The Roman Catholic Church in Canada is on record as favoring repeal of the anticontraception statute, not because of any compromise with Catholic principles, but because the law is unenforceable and hypocritical. Said Canada's Roman Catholic bishops in 1966: "A large number of our fellow citizens believe that this law violates their rights to be informed and helped toward responsible parenthood in accordance with their

[1] Editor's note: This means 19.4 births per thousand population.

personal beliefs." (Canadians confidently expect the law to be repealed this year.)

Significantly, retail sales of oral contraceptives in Canada last year were estimated at $30 million. However, drugstore owners do not consider this a windfall of profits. "Sales of contraceptives," says the head of one drug chain, "also cut down on sales of diapers, baby foods, medicines, and other things." And Canada's largest manufacturer of baby carriages reports: "We've had a big drop in business even in Catholic Quebec. French Canadians aren't having those fifth and sixth babies as they did in the old days."

International planned-parenthood hopes today are high but realistic. The movement is organized, and a good beginning has been made. But a tremendous job remains to be done; there are vast pockets of poverty, illiteracy, and, specifically, ignorance of modern contraception even in the advanced Western nations. The Planned Parenthood Federation of America, for example, reported in 1966: "Studies have confirmed that about half the children born to ADC mothers (i.e., the four million cases now receiving government Aid to Dependent Children) and 90 per cent of those born out of wedlock were the result of unwanted pregnancies."

Dr. Leona Baumgartner of the State Department's Agency for International Development has made several surveys of family planning around the world. She spells out the objectives of the IPPF movement: "The goal is not just fewer people. It is to give greater opportunity to all for a fuller life—a chance for freedom from hunger, disease, ignorance and poverty, for development of their own innate capacities, and for helping their children. To achieve these goals, many people want smaller families. Effective methods are available. Their widespread application comes next."

The consensus now is that a "world of wanted children" is no longer a dream, but a goal well within the reach of people of good will.

Part III
GOVERNMENT'S ROLE
IN FAMILY PLANNING

10

STATEMENT OF CATHOLIC
BISHOPS AND REPLIES

*The following statement on "The Government and Birth Control" was
issued after approval, "without audible dissent," by the body of U.S.
Catholic bishops at their annual meeting at the Catholic University of
America in Washington, D.C., on Monday, November 14, 1966:*

The good of the individual person and that of human society are intimately bound up with the stability of the family. Basic to the well-
being of the family is freedom from external coercion in order that it
may determine its own destiny.

This freedom involves inherent personal and family rights, including
the freedom and responsibility of spouses to make conscientious decisions in terms of nuptial love, determination of family size, and the
rearing of children. The Church and the state must play supportive
roles, fostering conditions in modern society which will help the family
achieve the fullness of its life and mission as the means ordained by
God for bringing the person into being and maturity.

We address ourselves here to certain questions of concern to the
family, with special reference to public policies related to social conditions and the problems of our times.

In so doing, we speak in the light of the pastoral constitution on

The Church in the Modern World adopted by Vatican Council II. Faced with our government's stepped-up intervention in family planning, including the subsidizing of contraceptive programs at home and abroad, we feel bound in conscience to recall particularly the solemn warning expressed in these words:

". . . [There] are many today who maintain that the increase in world population, or at least the population increase in some countries, mus⁴ be radically curbed by every means possible and by any kind of intervention on the part of public authority. In view of this contention, the Council urges everyone to guard against solutions, whether publicly or privately supported, or at times even imposed, which are contrary to the moral law. For in keeping with man's inalienable right to marry and generate children, the decision concerning the number of children they will have depends on the correct judgment of the parents and it can in no way be left to the judgment of public authority." (*The Church in the Modern World*, Section 2, Number 87.)

Therefore, a major preoccupation in our present statement must be with the freedom of spouses to determine the size of their families. It is necessary to underscore this freedom because in some current efforts of government—federal and state—to reduce poverty, we see welfare programs increasingly proposed which include threats to the free choice of spouses. Just as freedom is undermined when poverty and disease are present, so, too, is freedom endangered when persons who control welfare benefits or represent public authority presume to influence the decision as to the number of children or the frequency of births in a family.

Free decision is curtailed when spouses feel constrained to choose birth limitation because of poverty, inadequate and inhuman housing, or lack of proper medical services. Here we insist that it is the positive duty of government to help bring about those conditions of family freedom which will relieve spouses from such material and physical pressures to limit family size.

Government promotion of family-planning programs as part of tax-supported relief projects may easily result in the temptation and finally the tragic decision to reduce efforts to foster the economic, social, and indeed moral reforms needed to build the free, enlightened society.

In connection with present and proposed governmental family-limitation programs, there is frequently the implication that freedom is assured so long as spouses are left at liberty to choose among different methods of birth control. This we reject as a narrow concept of freedom. Birth control is not a universal obligation, as is often implied; moreover, true freedom of choice must provide even for those who wish to raise a larger family without being subject to criticism and without forfeiting for themselves the benefits or for their children the educational opportunities which have become part of the value system of a truly free society. We reject, most emphatically, the suggestion that any family should be adjudged too poor to have the children it conscientiously desires.

The freedom of spouses to determine the size of their families must not be inhibited by any conditions upon which relief or welfare assistance is provided. Health and welfare assistance should not be linked even indirectly, to conformity with a public agency's views on family limitation or birth control; nor may the right to found a large family be brought properly into question because it contradicts current standards arbitrarily deducted from general population statistics. No government social worker or other representative of public power should in any way be permitted to impose his judgment, in a matter so close to personal values and to the very sources of life, upon the family seeking assistance; neither should he be permitted to initiate suggestions placing, even by implication, public authority behind the recommendation that new life in a family should be prevented.

For these reasons, we have consistently urged and we continue to urge, as a matter of sound public policy, a clear and unqualified separation of welfare assistance from birth control considerations—whatever the legality or morality of contraception in general or in specific forms—in order to safeguard the freedom of the person and the autonomy of the family.

On previous occasions we have warned of dangers to the right of privacy posed by governmental birth-control programs; we have urged upon government a role of neutrality whereby it neither penalizes nor promotes birth control. Recent developments, however, show government rapidly abandoning any such role. Far from merely seeking to provide information in response to requests from the needy, government activities increasingly seek aggressively to persuade and even coerce the underprivileged to practice birth control. In this, government far exceeds its proper role. The citizen's right to decide without pressure is now threatened. Intimate details of personal, marital, and family life are suddenly becoming the province of government officials in programs of assistance to the poor. We decry this overreaching by government and assert again the inviolability of the right of human privacy.

We support all needed research toward medically and morally acceptable methods which can assist spouses to make responsible and generous decisions in seeking to co-operate with the will of God in what pertains to family size and well-being. A responsible decision will always be one which is open to life rather than intent upon the prevention of life; among religious people, it includes a strong sense of dependence upon God's providence.

It should be obvious that a full understanding of human worth, personal and social, will not permit the nation to put the public power behind the pressures for a contraceptive way of life. We urge government, at all levels, to resist pressures toward any merely mathematical and negative effort to solve health or population problems. We call upon all—and especially Catholics—to oppose, vigorously and by every democratic means, those campaigns already underway in some states and at the national level toward the active promotion, by tax-supported agencies, of birth prevention as a public policy, above all in connection with welfare benefit programs. History has shown that as a people lose respect for any life and a positive and generous attitude toward new life, they move fatally to inhuman infanticide, abortion, sterilization, and euthanasia; we fear that history is, in fact, repeating itself on this point within our own land at the moment.

Our government has a laudable history of dedication to the cause of freedom. In the service of this cause it is currently embarked upon a massive, unprecedented program of aid to underdeveloped nations. Through imaginative and constructive efforts, it shows itself willing to do battle with the enemies of freedom, notably poverty and ignorance. We gladly encourage our government to press this struggle with all the resources at its disposal and pledge our co-operation in all the ways in which we or those responsive to our leadership can be of assistance. Our nation's duty to assist underdeveloped countries flows from the divine law that the goods of the earth are destined for the well-being of all the human race.

In the international field, as in the domestic field, financial assistance must not be linked to policies which pressure for birth limitation. We applaud food-supply programs of foreign aid which condition our co-operation on evidence that the nations benefited pledge themselves to develop their own resources; we deplore any linking of aid by food or money to conditions, overt or oblique, involving prevention of new life. Our country is not at liberty to impose its judgment upon another, either as to the growth of the latter or as to the size of its families.

Insofar as it does so, our country is being cast in the role of a foreign power using its instrumentalities to transgress intimate *mores* and alter the moral cultures of other nations rather than in the historic American role of offering constructive, unselfish assistance to people in need. Indeed, we are aware of existing apprehension in the minds of many of the peoples of the world that the United States, in its own great affluence, is attempting, by seeking to limit their populations, to avoid its moral responsibility to help other peoples help themselves precisely that they may grow in healthy life, generous love, and in all the goods which presuppose and enrich both life and love.

Programs inhibiting new life, above all when linked to offers of desperately needed aid, are bound to create eventual resentment in any upon whom we even seem to impose them and will ultimately be gravely detrimental to the image, the moral prestige, and the basic interests of the United States.

Obviously, therefore, international programs of aid should not be conditioned upon acceptance of birth-control programs by beneficiary nations. Equally obvious, however, should be the fact that, in the practical administration of overseas assistance, neither direct nor indirect pressures should be exerted by our personnel to affect the choice of spouses as to the number of children in their family. In the international field, as in the domestic field, both our government in its policy and American representatives in their work should strive above all to bring about those economic and social advances which will make possible for spouses conscientious family planning without resort to contraceptive procedures fostered among them by controversial policies backed by American political power and financial aid.

Sobering lessons of history clearly teach that only those nations remain stable and vigorous whose citizens have and are encouraged to keep high regard for the sanctity and autonomy of family life among themselves and among the peoples who depend in any way upon them. Let our political leaders be on guard that the common good suffer no evil from public policies which tamper with the instincts of love and the sources of life.

REPLY OF DEPARTMENT OF HEALTH, EDUCATION, AND WELFARE

On November 15, 1966, the Department of Health, Education, and Welfare replied, through its assistant secretary, Dr. Philip R. Lee, to the statement of the Catholic bishops issued the preceding day.

The Department of Health, Education, and Welfare, in all of its programs, is seeking the same goals of family integrity, well-being, and freedom from external coercion as those stated in the bishops' statement.

In Secretary Gardner's policy statement on population dynamics, fertility, sterility, and family planning issued last January, he said:

"The objectives of the departmental policy are to improve the health of the people, to strengthen the integrity of the family, and to provide families the freedom of choice to determine the spacing of their children and the size of their families. Programs conducted or supported by the department shall guarantee freedom from coercion or pressure of mind or conscience. The department will make known to state and local agencies that funds are available for [family-planning] programs."

These policies apply to all of the family-planning programs conducted or supported by the department, whether through the Public Health Service or the Children's Bureau.

The purpose of the department's policies and programs in the area of family planning is to provide all citizens with the freedom to choose or not to choose family planning and, in addition, the freedom to choose among all of the alternative methods of family planning if they so desire. Specific assurances are required that failure to accept family-planning services will not jeopardize a family's right to financial assistance.

Although this freedom has existed generally for wealthy and middle-income persons, it has not existed, in actual fact, for most poor persons because family-planning services either did not exist in their areas or because they could not afford those which did exist.

The purpose of the department's programs in family planning is not to deny freedom but to extend it. We seek to make available to all Americans a freedom which is already available to most Americans.

The decision as to whether to have publicly supported family-planning services is a decision which is made not at the federal level but at the state or local level. As the secretary indicated in his policy statement, this department will bring no pressure to have such services established. And if a state or community elects to provide such services, the department will not provide financial support unless the services guarantee both freedom from coercion and the freedom to choose among all alternative methods of family planning.

In a telephone conversation with me today, Secretary Gardner stated: "In the development of our policies, we have been in continuous communication with representatives of the National Catholic Welfare Conference. I personally extended to their representatives an invitation to bring to my attention any specific examples of coercion that they encountered. Since I extended this invitation, approximately eight or nine months ago, no examples have been brought to my attention."

To the best of our knowledge, the letter to which the Most Rev. Raymond J. Gallagher [1] referred was never received by the Department of Health, Education, and Welfare. We would be pleased to meet with Bishop Gallagher and other officials of the Church at any time to receive their views and the expression of their concerns.

REPLY OF OFFICE OF ECONOMIC OPPORTUNITY

On November 15, 1966, the Office of Economic Opportunity through its director, Sargent Shriver, replied to the statement of the Catholic bishops.

Upon application from local communities, OEO has made grants of Community Action program funds to assist in providing information, medical services, and supplies for family-planning projects.

---

[1] Editor's note: Bishop Gallagher served as a representative of the National Catholic Welfare Conference.

Every one of these grants has been made subject to legally enforceable conditions which prohibit the community operating the family-planning project from forcing anyone in any way to receive family-planning information or assistance.

Every participant in an OEO-financed family-planning project must be a voluntary recipient of the service. Coercion or compulsion is specifically forbidden.

It is also specifically forbidden to make participation in an OEO-financed family-planning program a requirement before a poor person can obtain any other benefit or service.

These administrative requirements, imposed by OEO, have now been incorporated into the Economic Opportunity Act by a recent amendment. It should be emphasized, however, that they have been mandatory preconditions since OEO's very first grant in family planning.

Any allegation that any OEO grant for family planning has been used to force information or service on any person, or as a prerequisite for other services, will be immediately investigated. If found true, prompt remedial action will be taken.

To my knowledge, no such allegation has ever been made and substantiated with regard to any of the seventy-two Community Action components for family planning OEO has funded to date.

PROMINENT AMERICANS PROTEST BISHOPS' STATEMENT

Greatly concerned over the effect that the bishops' statement might have upon the efforts of our government to deal constructively with the problem of the world's soaring population, the Hugh Moore Fund issued a reply, published as a full-page ad in the December 18, 1966, issue of the New York Times *and in other newspapers.*

The reply was signed by seventy-eight prominent Americans, including some of our most noted scientists, educators, theologians, physicians, demographers, churchmen, statesmen, authors, businessmen, editors, gynecologists, and Nobel prize winners. The reply took direct issue with the statement of the bishops and urged individuals and organizations to speak out quickly in support of the government's present program.

CATHOLIC BISHOPS ASSAIL BIRTH CONTROL AS MILLIONS FACE STARVATION

The charges of the Roman Catholic bishops on November 14, 1966, add up to a frontal attack on organized family planning. The bishops called upon everyone "to oppose, vigorously and by every democratic means, those campaigns already underway in some states and at the national level toward the active promotion, by tax-supported agencies, of birth prevention as a public policy, above all in connection with welfare benefit programs."

This aggressive move was made notwithstanding the known facts respecting the population explosion which President Johnson has called "humanity's greatest challenge."

Tidal Wave of People

A tidal wave of *three billion* more people will inundate the earth in the next thirty years, *if the present rate of increase is not arrested!* The population of the United States may increase by 150 million!

Famine already stalks the earth. India, kept from the brink by U.S. wheat shipments, will add 200 millions more people by 1980. "The world is on the threshold of the biggest famine in history," concludes Dr. Raymond Ewell, former adviser to the government of India. Dr. Ewell predicts famine in India, Pakistan, and Communist China about 1970, and in Brazil, Egypt, Indonesia, and Turkey shortly after.

The bishops' accusation goes beyond their unsupported charges of coercion of women on welfare. It encompasses all family planning, *domestic and international.* It strikes at "our government's stepped-up intervention in family planning, including the subsidizing of contraceptive programs at home and abroad."

World Catastrophe in Prospect

If the bishops succeed in their attempt: 1. Millions of women on welfare will be deprived of the knowledge and effective methods of preventing the birth of children they cannot care for. 2. Through fear of reprisal at the polls, state legislators may hold back welfare funds for family planning, thereby increasing the tax burden of unwanted children. 3. Federal administrators, whose "stepped-up" programs the bishops have attacked, may cut or diminish these programs. 4. The President of the United States himself is threatened by the bishops' warning that *"our public officials be on guard."* 5. Congressmen may hesitate to advance the program on foreign aid in the population field so splendidly begun by the 89th Congress. Without population control the huge *$7 billion* Food for Peace Program will be a mere stopgap, saving the lives of those who would produce still more hungry people.

"Either we take the fullest measures both to raise productivity and to stabilize population growth, or we face a disaster of unprecedented magnitude," according to Dr. B. R. Sen, director-general of the United Nations Food and Agriculture Organization.

If such measures are not taken, it is likely that Americans—a humane people—may be rationing the food on their own tables in the not distant future.

Public Favors Birth Control

John F. Kennedy was the first U.S. President to concern himself officially with the problem of population limitation. The bishops' attack has been read by enlightened Catholic leaders with a sense of unbelief and dismay. They have called it unrealistic, out-of-date, reactionary, and inconsistent with the spirit of Vatican II in the modern world. Professor William D'Antonio of Notre Dame University referred to the bishops' statement as "beating a dead horse."

Asked in a Gallup survey last year if birth control information ought to be easily available to any married person wanting it, *81 per cent of Catholics and 86 per cent of non-Catholics said YES.*

The Battle Will Be Won

The National Academy of Sciences, the nation's leading scientific body, has declared that "the population problem can be successfully attacked by developing new methods of fertility regulation and implementing programs of voluntary family planning widely and rapidly throughout the world."

The magnitude of the challenge, however, is so great that only government can meet it fully. The National Council of Churches has come out against any government curtailment of "its efforts to provide increasingly adequate services for all families or governments where such services are desired."

Individuals and organizations should speak out quickly in vigorous support of the government's present program. Contact federal, state, and city officials. Point out that the American people—Catholics, Protestants, and Jews—are overwhelmingly behind the program, as every poll shows.

Birth control is a popular cause which can be supported confidently. If in the years to come the earth should be ravished by the fabled horsemen of the Apocalypse—war, famine, disease, and death—let the responsibility not be ours.

NATIONAL COUNCIL OF CHURCHES COMMENTS

The reaction of the National Council of Churches to the issues raised by the statement approved by the Catholic bishops was expressed in a statement released on November 15, 1966, over the signature of Dr. R. H. Edwin Espy, general secretary of the NCC. The full text follows:

While we concur with the statements of the Catholic bishops of the United States about the moral freedom of a couple to choose the size of their family, we think it unfortunate that their statement went beyond warning to actual accusation of coercion by governmental agencies. No instances of such pressure have been brought to our attention.

Free decision regarding family planning is often curtailed by the lack of adequate information and services. The National Council of Churches has spoken clearly on behalf of the right of all couples to have access to such information and services. Only then can there be a free decision to use or not to use according to the dictates of one's own conscience.

Birth control is not a universal obligation, but responsible parenthood most certainly is. This includes the proper spacing of children to preserve the health and welfare of the mother and of the total family. Birth-control services for child spacing are a vital need in any program promoting family health and stability.

We sincerely hope that no government agency will curtail its efforts to provide increasingly adequate services for all families or governments where such services are desired.

BISHOP HINES SPEAKS

On November 22, 1966, shortly after the Catholic bishops issued their statement, the presiding bishop of the Episcopal Church in the United States, the Right Rev. John E. Hines, declared that the Episcopal Church through its General Convention fully supports the United States Government in its efforts to render assistance in population control both within the United States and in other nations. He revealed that birth-control clinics are currently being sponsored by the Episcopal Church both within the United States and overseas.

The Episcopal Church and the bishops of the whole Anglican Communion have clearly expressed vigorous support of world-wide programs of population control. I call attention to an action of our Church's General Convention of 1961, which outlines our position on these matters:

"Whereas warnings against the explosive results of world population increase . . . have raised with new urgency questions of the morality of restricting population growth through birth control measures and planned parenthood; and

"Whereas the archbishops and bishops of the Anglican Communion have defined their position on this question . . . and

"Whereas the General Convention wishes to affirm this position . . . therefore be it

"Resolved that . . . this General Convention holds that family planning in such ways as are mutually acceptable to husband and wife in Christian conscience . . . is a right and important factor in Christian family life. Such responsible parenthood, built on obedience to all the duties of marriage, requires a wise stewardship of the resources and abilities of the family as well as a thoughtful consideration of the varying population needs and problems of society and the claims of future generations."

The General Convention further urged the United States Government to render assistance to population-control programs of other nations which request aid:

"This General Convention holds that it is the duty of the better developed countries such as our own to help countries to become self-supporting in food supplies and health measures through technical and other aids. In particular, while condemning abortion and infanticide, we believe that methods of control which are medically endorsed and morally acceptable may help the people of these lands so to plan family life that children may be born without a likelihood of starvation, and we approve the rendering by our government of assistance to this end wherever it is officially sought."

This action was reinforced by the 1964 General Convention, which instructed the Church's national Executive Council to study, with the aid of outside experts, what more the Protestant Episcopal Church can do to bring about effective birth control throughout the world. As part of this effort, pilot birth-control clinics are currently being sponsored in places both overseas and inside the United States by our Church. I am requesting that the Presiding Bishops' Fund for World Relief double the funds made available for this program in the immediate years ahead.

Less than a month ago, the House of Bishops of our Church, meeting in Wheeling, West Virginia, reiterated the urgency of this concern, in a Statement on Population, Poverty, and Peace. I now commend this statement . . . to your attention.

Statement of Episcopal Bishops on Population Control
Wheeling, West Virginia, October 25, 1966

At the beginning of the Christian era, there were three hundred million human beings on the earth. Not until 1820 did that figure reach one billion. A hundred years later, it doubled to two billion. In forty more years, in 1960, it passed three billion. By the year 2000, it should be well above six billion or twice as many people as are living today. Every year the world's population grows by fifty to sixty million people, roughly the population of France, or the United Kingdom, or the whole Roman Empire at the time Christ was born.

These figures have become commonplace. It is nearly impossible to clothe them in flesh and blood, or to comprehend the stark facts of the human tragedy around the globe which accompany them. Two thirds of the present world population live in nutritional deficiency.

One billion men, women, and children daily suffer crippling hunger. Food production has not kept pace with population in the underdeveloped nations. Food supply will have to be more than *doubled* in the next two decades merely to preserve the present subsistence level. Thus catastrophic famine is likely in the early 1970s in India, Pakistan, and China, followed in a few short years by Indonesia, Iran, Turkey, Egypt, and by 1980 in most of the other countries of Asia, Africa, and Latin America.

However extensive the promotion of family planning, in the near future, the explosive population growth will bring the world shortly to a food crisis of mammoth proportions, one which poses inescapable threats to the stability and growth of the nations and to the peace of the whole world.

Few citizens with a concern for public affairs can have escaped a presentation of these facts. Yet they recede into the background of our consciences, simultaneously perceived and ignored with that same detachment with which we regard the possibility of nuclear war. It is not that men are notably callous about human suffering, failing through lack of moral courage to grasp the personal, family, and community tragedies hidden in these bare statistics.

It is not that Christians and others who affirm the solidarity of mankind have not sought through governments, through the United Nations, and by a wealth of voluntary effort to minister within the calamitous conditions we confront. Rather the issues have not yet become the major agenda of mankind or of the Church.

God who created human life wills that we give ourselves to the relief of suffering and to the cause of justice and peace. That truth is central to our Gospel. The command, "Feed the hungry," then, must have an overriding priority in our corporate and personal lives.

All the answers to the problems of overpopulation, hunger, and poverty are not known. But there are things which the Church can do. To obey the will of our Lord, let us give primary stress to meeting human need wherever encountered in our missionary enterprise overseas through use of both new and existing resources of personnel and facilities for the development of agriculture, welfare, and medical services, education, and economic growth. Let us conduct our programs in a manner which is indigenous both in methodology and the human resources developed. Let us undertake these efforts in concert with other Anglicans, other Christians, other religious and secular agencies in these lands; and thus, by such effort in meeting human need, make real the meaning and intent of "mutual responsibility and interdependence."

We affirm also and support programs of population control, recognizing and proclaiming that the population explosion has become a world crisis in which personal responsibility affects all strata of society. Family planning is not only for those who are poor but also for all who could accept social responsibility seriously. We therefore support the availability to all of legitimate birth-control services within the United States and the creation overseas of pilot programs which may persuade people and governments that such programs on a larger scale are practical and effective. . . .

CENTRAL CONFERENCE OF AMERICAN RABBIS

Following the publication of the Catholic bishops' statement, Rabbi Jacob J. Weinstein of Chicago, president of the 970-member Central Conference of American Rabbis, issued in behalf of his organization the following statement:

"We believe that the government has the right and obligation to make access to planned-parenthood information available to all who seek it. We see no coercion in government and welfare agencies providing such information. We believe the welfare of our country and of the world depends greatly on the ability to maintain a balance between food supply of the world and its population."

"FREEDOM IMPERILED": THE CHRISTIAN CENTURY

The Christian Century of November 30, 1966, ran an editorial, "Did the Bishops Blunder?", in which it said in part:

We understand that the government's reply is that freedom is imperiled when official representatives of the Church make sweeping charges without producing a single bit of concrete evidence proving their allegations . . . If the bishops produce convincing proof that the poor are being coerced by the government into using birth-control devices, we shall take our stand with them. But until they do so, we have to say that freedom is imperiled when any large bloc of the country, religious or otherwise, condemns and threatens the government without concrete evidence that the government is guilty as charged.

11

CATHOLIC DISAGREEMENT
WITH BISHOPS' STATEMENT

What was the reaction of the Catholic press? As most Catholic news-papers and magazines are published under the supervision of ecclesias-tical authority, few have the liberty to deal objectively and critically with the policies, programs, and decisions of bishops. This is the great weakness of the Catholic press, for without freedom the press becomes the voice of authority, of the officials of the Church, but not necessarily of the thought and sentiments of the vast majority of its members. Virtually the only publications which are free from censorship and hence have the freedom to speak their minds on all the vital issues confronting the Church today are two weeklies, edited by laymen: Commonweal *and* The National Catholic Reporter.

The editors of Commonweal *reacted sharply to the statement on birth control "coercion" in their lead editorial "Regressive Statement," in the December 2, 1966, issue. The portion dealing with this topic follows:*

The birth-control statement was poorly thought out and regressive. It was also disingenuous in purporting to be a simple expression of con-cern for the right of privacy, when the language and arguments made clear enough what the bishops declined to say directly: that they opposed birth-control programs because they oppose birth control itself as immoral. Was it intended as a holding action—a way of launching a major attack on government birth-control programs without stating in emphatic moral terms what the bishops may have to retract if the Pope changes his mind on the inherent immorality of contraception?

At the very least the bishops are open to this charge. And a line or two about the right of individuals to contraception data if they want it —which would have made the statement more credible—was pointedly excluded. The general lack of thoughtfulness that marked the statement came out clearly in the press conference. The bishops charged that the government had not even replied to their letter on birth-control programs, yet the bishops were unable to produce a copy of the letter, or even to remember to whom it had been sent.

After the bishops attacked government programs in general for invading privacy, and after both HEW and OEO responded for the government by pointing to specific safeguards in the law to guard against such violations of privacy, Bishop Gallagher said in behalf of his fellow bishops that he was talking about dangers in implementing the programs, not the programs themselves. Secretary Garner of HEW then told the press he had asked the National Catholic Welfare Conference to bring to his attention any specific examples of coercion (and had received no reply), whereupon Bishop Gallagher lamely replied that he didn't think the Church nationally should get into documentation of particulars. One would think a charge so serious ought to be documented.

In their statement, the bishops drew a picture of the government imposing its will on fearful and unprotected welfare recipients. Welfare recipients are abused often enough by welfare workers, but the picture here does not accord with reality. Surveys show that recipients want fewer children than nonrecipients, but don't know how to prevent unwanted pregnancies.

The December 10, 1966, issue of America, *the weekly publication of Jesuits of the United States and Canada, carries a commentary by Mary McGrory, entitled "The Bishops' Controversial Declaration." The text follows:*

Administration officials who had been enjoying the era of good feeling between government and Church that was born with the end of the long controversy over federal aid to parochial schools were surprised and put out by the recent declaration of the bishops on government birth-control programs.

The bishops' insistence on "freedom from coercion" in these programs is not only widely shared by the most ardent advocates of birth control; it is written into rigid guidelines that regulate the activities of the Health, Education, and Welfare Department and the Office of Economic Opportunity in this field.

It was not merely the contents of the statement that caused officials to be miffed. They did not understand why the bishops had not brought violations to their attention before making charges that were never specified beyond a designation of certain welfare officials who were committed to a "contraceptive way of life."

Said one White House aide: "Our door is always open to the National Catholic Welfare Conference. Their representatives have been in and out of here steadily working on parochial school problems. I wish they had brought this up with us."

For OEO Director Sargent Shriver, an outstanding Catholic official, the statement was an occasion of consternation. As a deeply committed member of his Church, he had spent many hours working out with representatives of the hierarchy regulations that—he pointed out in rebuttal—are legally enforceable and have not, to his knowledge, been violated in OEO.

In some quarters, the bishops' appeal to all faiths to help safeguard the privacy of the poor was interpreted as an excuse to restate the Catholic position on artificial contraception, which, as is well known, has not changed. The privacy of the poor is rather thoroughly invaded by every agency, public or private, through the applications they must fill out before they can even hope to obtain help.

James Reston, writing in the New York *Times*, saw the statement as a reflection of "the increasing tendencies of Pope Paul to rebuke the more progressive elements in the Catholic Church."

Whatever the reason for the bishops' declaration, it seemed at variance with the spirit evidenced in 1965, when no protest of consequence was registered at President Johnson's State of the Union announcement of his intention to work intensively on population-control problems.

In any case, the statement caused a great deal of controversy and overshadowed what were widely regarded as stirring pronouncements on race relations and the importance of seeking peace in Vietnam.

Under a Houston dateline of November 30, 1966, the Religious News Service carried the following news release:

A Jesuit priest who is chairman of the Section on Family Law of the American Bar Association has called the American bishops' statement on birth control and welfare "meaningless, unjust, and basically wrong."

Father Robert F. Drinan, S.J., dean of the Boston College Law School, member of the Bar of the State of Massachusetts and District of Columbia, told the Catholic Physicians Guild of Houston that he "does not understand the statement and the alleged allegations."

"The people need a better statement," he said in commenting on the bishops' charge that tying birth control and welfare programs together brought government pressures on needy couples.

Father Drinan is visiting professor at the Law School of the University of Texas. He is also assisting the Texas Bar Association in its attempt to rewrite the laws of the state concerning family and marriage.

In an interview with the *Texas Catholic Herald*, he issued a full explanation of his position concerning the statement issued by the bishops on November 14. Following is the text of Father Drinan's statement:

The most serious misunderstandings will almost inevitably result from lack of clarity and specificity in the statement of the Catholic bishops of America issued on November 14, 1966.

The statement affirms some splendid principles, but at the same time makes so many undocumented accusations against unnamed individuals or agencies that the whole document may only further confuse an already complex subject.

One excellent principle which is enunciated is the bishops' assertion that: "It is the positive duty of government to help bring about those conditions of family freedom which will relieve spouses from . . . material and physical pressures to limit family size." These "pressures" are listed as "poverty, inadequate and inhuman housing, and lack of proper medical care."

The accusations, however, dominate the text. It is stated that "governmental birth-control programs are not following the role of neutrality" previously recommended by the bishops. This neutrality is defined by the bishops as a role whereby government "neither penalizes nor promotes birth control."

One must assume therefore that the government is not required to be silent about birth control since this would clearly be penalizing birth control. The "government" (federal, state, or both?) is decried by the bishops as "overreaching" because "governmental activities increasingly seek aggressively to persuade and even coerce the underprivileged to practice birth control."

Again without any specificity and actually in an incomprehensible charge the bishops' statement asserts that "in some current efforts of government, federal and state, to reduce poverty, we see welfare programs increasingly proposed which include threats to the free choice of spouses." No evidence is offered as to the nature or location of the alleged "threats."

The role of government in relation to family solidarity is an enormously complicated one. It will not be clarified or implemented by ambiguous allegations that the state is invading the privacy of marriage and is adding to "the pressures for a contraceptive way of life."

In the November 23, 1966, issue, The National Catholic Reporter *carried the following editorial under the heading "Starting with Mistakes":*

After much reflection, carried on in a mood of determined optimism, we find it possible to offer two faintly favorable remarks on the U.S. bishops' statement dealing with birth control and public policy: 1. The statement does not represent the considered judgment of the whole body of bishops. 2. Probably no future statement on this or any other issue will incorporate all the mistakes built into this one.

These hopeful aspects can be dwelt upon a bit further, but honesty requires that the mistakes be examined first.

Timing: The public had been told that the bishops were gathering to tool up for the postconciliar era, but their first reported action was the issuance of one more statement cast in the familiar precouncil mode of denunciation and protest. In the news media the statement's serious charges, "unanimously" supported by the bishops, inevitably got the heaviest play, thereby downgrading the far more meaningful work done in the elections held the same day. One is led to suggest that an elementary course in public relations be made a prerequisite for consecration.

Procedure: First, the outgoing administrative board brought the statement to a vote, though supposedly its only remaining function was to conduct the elections. Second, the bishops had scant time to study and discuss the statement. Third, the decision was taken by voice vote, with mini-seconds permitted for the "nays" to register. Fourth, the vote was first announced—and therefore reported to the world—as unanimous, though in fact some bishops abstained. (Later "unanimous" was revised to "without audible dissent.") Fifth, it went unreported that after the vote at least one bishop voiced a vigorous protest against the procedure.

Evidence: The statement charges that government agencies are tyrannizing over the poor, forcing them to practice birth control or risk the loss of welfare benefits. No evidence supporting this very grave charge was offered. Despite the denials of federal officials, despite the anti-coercion safeguards written into the laws, it's conceivable that instances of coercion have occurred. But possibility is not fact, and any accusation of serious political abuses should rest on demonstrable facts. We can see no reason why clergymen should be exempt from this requirement of honest political discourse.

Content: The bishops' statement professes not to be concerned with the morality of contraception, but rather with political rights and principles—freedom of conscience, family autonomy, the right of privacy. It argues that spouses have an absolute right to determine the size of their own families—and government must not only refrain from interfering with this right, it should help poor couples who want large families by helping them overcome the poverty that cancels out their freedom.

But the pressures of poverty operate also on poor couples who want small families, and if the role of government is to help families make their choice in freedom, the logical deduction from the bishops' own argument is that government should help such couples by supplying them with information about birth control methods and with the means to apply them. The failure to acknowledge this obvious corollary makes the bishops' statement appear disingenuous.

The same criticism applies to the statement's profession of concern over the invasions of privacy which the bishops find in any government-assisted birth-control program. This is, as we have acknowledged, a real possibility. But outrageous abuses of privacy have been occurring for decades in connection with other welfare programs without ever drawing this kind of protest from the American hierarchy. In these circumstances the citizens of the nation are not likely to conclude that this statement was in fact forced from the bishops by their overriding concern for freedom. The more likely conclusion is that the bishops are still fighting birth control, and using for their purpose an argument that rests on concealed premises. In unguarded candor at last Monday's press conference, Archbishop Philip Hannan as much as admitted this by saying that the statement contains an implicit condemnation of contraception.

Taking all these factors into account, the statement has to be described as a disaster. Taking the long view, however, it's a mitigated disaster. On the record the statement is the responsibility of the whole body of bishops, and it is not exactly encouraging that despite its very serious defects of substance and procedure, no bishop was willing to make known his discontent. But in fact the statement is the work of only part of the U.S. bishops; it is not likely to have any great number of ardent defenders; it will not affect the substance of policy.

It may even achieve some of its professed aim by making welfare personnel more wary about anything that might smack of coercion in birth-control policies. The same effect could have been achieved, however, by a more moderate and better documented statement without hurting the Church's reputation for candor and responsibility. Maybe this lesson will be absorbed; if so, the very painfulness of this episode could be its most valuable aspect.

Commonweal, *in its December 2, 1966, issue, carried the following article, "Birth Control and Coercion," by Dr. William V. D'Antonio, chairman of the department of sociology at the University of Notre Dame:*

One of the major surprises of the recent meeting of the Catholic bishops in Washington was that they chose to issue, at the very outset, a strong denunciation of the Johnson administration's efforts in the area of family planning. "Far from merely seeking to provide information in response to requests from the needy," the bishops charged, "government activities increasingly seek aggressively to persuade and even coerce the underprivileged to practice birth control." This trend, they argued in their statement, threatens "the free choice of spouses" to determine the size of their families and seriously endangers the "inviolability of the right of human privacy." In sum, "government far exceeds its proper role."

Needless to say, the bishops' statement caught many unprepared, especially administration officials. They should not have been so surprised, for the bishops' statement only followed hard on the heels of an earlier and very similar statement by Bishop John Wright of Pittsburgh and a concerted campaign by the Catholic bishops of Pennsylvania. I want to focus my remarks on family planning and government policy around Bishop Wright's earlier statement, especially since he has long been thought of in Catholic circles as a progressive. Thus, his position cannot easily be dismissed as intransigent conservatism, something many might be prone to do with the statement of the American bishops as a whole.

In reaction to an announcement in Pittsburgh last May that the city would begin financing planned-parenthood clinics, Bishop Wright said: "Directly moral considerations apart, the introduction of government power, policy, and money into intimate family relations, especially those involving the expression of nuptial love and the sources of life, constitutes a clear peril to basic values, beginning with freedom." The bishop went on to plead *for* government aid to help those already born to achieve personal autonomy and material well-being. Clearly, the bishop is not opposed to government aid *per se*, but only government aid which may make effective contraceptive practices possible—on the ground that human freedom would be jeopardized in the process.

This is essentially the position taken by the bishops in their Washington meeting, by spokesmen for the National Catholic Welfare Conference, and by the bishops of Pennsylvania in their more or less successful lobby against the recent Pennsylvania state government effort to institute broad-scale family-planning aid in that state. Yet while NCWC has lobbied forcefully against government-sponsored family-planning clinics, it has also forcefully argued for such government programs as aid which supposedly threatens human freedom, while the other aid is said to support and encourage freedom. In this important sense, the bishops, Bishop Wright, and NCWC are right: The basic issue is human freedom and how best to enhance it.

Human freedom consists in the ability to make choices. This means in the first place that there are a plurality of alternative choices available to an individual or group, and, secondly, that the individual or group is aware of the choices and informed about their consequences. The ability to make choices is rather narrowly restricted by what sociologists call the socialization process, the process by which an individual becomes a predictable, role-playing, group-conforming creature. Freedom is not a given, it isn't just there; it depends on the acquisition of knowledge about events and possible events and their consequences. And, I should add, it depends on the creative action of the individual to do something with this knowledge.

A major point to be made here is that the poor, the downtrodden, the underprivileged have little or no freedom—they lack *money* which permits certain kinds of choices, especially material choices; and they lack knowledge, language, ideas which permit a whole series of choices with social consequences. Government-sponsored family-planning clinics at home and abroad would provide them with knowledge and facilities, thus widening their range of choices and, as I see it, their freedom.

But the argument of those opposed to government-sponsored family planning goes deeper. *They* say that government action in this area is an invasion of the most sacred right of privacy, the privacy of the bedroom. Somehow, it is argued, government programs inevitably mean government coercion—and in this case, the end of bedroom freedom. The argument seems specious on several counts.

It is not, for one thing, self-evident that government aid to family-planning clinics would be more coercive than government aid to foster social security, medicare, college and university aid programs, and certainly aid to parochial schools. Who would be coerced? The word "coercion" in this context means that people are being forced to act against their will by people representing the government. The sociological data, from studies in the United States and abroad, show that people in the "deprived" sectors of the society would be glad to accept birth-control help if they could get it. I know of no study which shows the opposite.

Dr. Donald Bogue, one of the country's most respected demographers, reported on a 1959 study of low-income population in Chicago: "The most important finding was that despite their actual high fertility, these groups said they wanted smaller families than do more well-to-do people . . ." He also reported: "The incidence of unwanted pregnancy is very high among these low-income and low-education groups; nevertheless, they endorse the idea of family planning more strongly than does the general population." Dr. Alberto Lleras Camargo, twice president of Colombia, said recently that, "Our population simply cannot be allowed to grow at the savage rate of the present (between 2.5 and 3 per cent annually) . . . The humane, *Christian*, economic, and political solution is birth control. And the sooner the better."

Thus, the evidence at hand shows that these people won't be coerced. They will welcome the chance to have some freedom in this matter. Most of them live now in the unfreedom of ignorance. There may be coercion, not in the law as such, but in its implementation! But this is an empirical question to be answered by experience, not accepted as an *a priori* assumption.

Another point in regard to this charge of invasion of privacy is more challenging. Actions of people may be said to be private (that is, of their own but no one else's concern) insofar as they have no further social consequences. There may have been a time in the history of this country when the begetting and rearing of children were private concerns of individual couples. *This is not the case today.* In our complex society the begetting of children can have great societal consequences. Family fertility patterns are inextricably bound up in the affairs of society. Hence, if there is evidence that the common good of all is threatened by large-scale unplanned, unwanted procreation in slum conditions, then the society is justified in acting to protect itself. The question then becomes one of asking what kind of action is necessary and desirable.

1. There is no argument against government aid on the ground that procreation is an absolute good that must be fostered at all costs.

2. There is substantial evidence that unplanned, unwanted procreation is detrimental to those born under such conditions, to the parents (at least the mother), and to the society which pays the cost of lives unfulfilled, or lived out in deviancy from accepted patterns. Perhaps the most persuasive evidence is found in the rising abortion rates throughout the world.

3. This point seems to be well understood by the Christian Democrats of Chile. They believe that in a pluralistic society the government

should allow such programs for those who desire them. The Chilean women apparently desire them. The Christian Democrats of Chile appear to recognize population control as central to their aspirations for a better life for the Chilean people. The National Health Service is conducting an aggressive campaign against abortion, while permitting use of its facilities for birth-control services. It was reported that some twelve thousand IUDs were inserted during the past year.

There is an important additional point to be made; this involves the question of neutrality. Those opposing government action in family planning argue that the government should be neutral, that it has no business either promoting or discouraging family planning. I would disagree. The government is the agent *par excellence* for the people (i.e., society) by which they can promote their general welfare. In fact, given the size of the population involved, and the complex web of interrelationships which binds each to his fellows and makes it difficult if not impossible for any man or couple to be an island, the government should be concerned in this area of life.

Of course the dissemination of birth-control information is not neutral. To ask people to consider an alternative to what they are doing is not a neutral request. It implies value judgments about the alternative(s) to be suggested. Nonetheless, the argumental neutrality seems misplaced. Is the government neutral if it does not provide family-planning help? Or is it being negligent in its responsibilities? I would argue that it is neglecting its responsibility when it ignores an urgent problem which no other agency of the society can cope with. We know empirically that twenty to thirty million Americans live deprived lives, and that the conditions of life elsewhere in the world are as bad or worse for more than one billion people. Because this problem touches on sexuality, should the government thereby be neutral? Can it be? Why is this area more sacred than the starving, educationally deprived conditions of these people?

The opponents argue that this analogy is weak because birth control involves "the divinely conferred human personality, the mind of a person, the soul of a person, as well as the myriad strands of that person's relationship to other persons and to God." And these are no business of government, so they say. My response would be that God gives each person the potential of a mind and a personality, but that these potentials become human reality only when man interacts with his fellow man. Man is above all else social and he has created a social organization called the government, to help promote his well-being.

Here it seems clear in the present case that a vast majority of Americans approve of federal aid for family-planning clinics—65 per cent according to the Gallup Poll of October 1965. Furthermore, 59 per cent of American Catholics in this poll also approved of such aid. A majority also approved of using federal funds to support birth-control programs abroad.

Indications are that the federal government is taking the cue that it has the support of the majority of the American population and is going ahead with the development of birth-control programs both at home and abroad. Up to the present, the major focus of most activity, especially through the Children's Bureau and the National Institutes of Health, has been on basic research, with a large proportion of some seven million dollars in fiscal 1967 geared to research related to fertility reproductive physiology and studies of motivations and attitudes of potential clients toward family-planning services.

Probably the most important government source of aid for family-planning services is coming through the Office of Economic Opportunity. It has been estimated that some fifty projects had been founded through OEO to provide family-planning information and service to indigent women. It also appears clear that Title XIX of the Social Security Amendment Act of 1965 will become an important source of federal aid through state grants-in-aid in the years ahead. . . .

Thus, it would appear that even without such legislation as proposed in S1676 (the Gruening Bill to establish an Office of Population Affairs within HEW) and S2993 (the Tydings Bill to provide direct grants for family-planning services), the government has available legislation which permits a major confrontation with the problem, at least at home.

There are perhaps a minimum of five million medically indigent, fertile women in the United States who are in need of or could make use of family-planning services. In the year 1965, some three hundred thousand received help through public facilities; some two hundred thousand received service through Planned Parenthood Centers. Some four and one-half million remain unserved. Figured at the average cost of $20 per year per woman, family-planning services for this population would come to some ninety million dollars annually.

The current budget for health and medical services at all government levels is approximately $9 billion. Obviously, family-planning service for that segment of the population not able to afford it on its own does not appear to be an onerous additional burden in itself. It seems well within our ability to foster the opportunity for a "good life" for the children of poverty in this country, and the government has made a firm commitment in this direction.

The scene at the international level is much more complicated, but is not without hope. Most of the world's governments are now seeking help. At present, we can be most effective by providing the technical assistance that is needed just to develop policies and programs. As our commitments abroad through AID and other programs increase, we will have to expand considerably a wide range of professional skills, in obstetrics and gynecology, demography and sociology, and in agricultural and industrial technology. We can only hope to help others as they become aware of and perceive a need for help.

The situation in Latin America, for example, seems to be changing rapidly. As a result, we have been able to develop demographic institutes there, to get the basic information that is needed before any effective proposals can even be considered. In this effort, private foundations such as Ford, and organizations like International Planned Parenthood, can help, but, increasingly, the government has come to be recognized as the agent of society most capable of and responsible for confronting this problem.

Such then is the unfavorable reaction of that section of the Catholic press which is free to venture critical comment on the policy, decision, and actions of bishops.

12

CATHOLIC SCHOLARS
BACK GOVERNMENT AID

Prior to the issuance of the statement by the Catholic bishops on November 14, 1966, there were two notable statements by groups of Catholic scholars on the government's role in providing information and aid to persons seeking to regulate births in their families. They were widely publicized and should be cited here because they are impressive formulations of scholarly Catholic thought on this burning issue.

The first was the statement presented by Rev. Dexter L. Hanley, S.J., director of Law, Human Rights, and Social Values at Georgetown University, to the Family Law Section of the American Bar Association at its convention in Miami, Florida, on August 9, 1965. His statement was supported by the signatures of fifty-six other Catholic scholars, many of whom are experts in political and social sciences and other relevant disciplines.

STATEMENT OF REV. DEXTER L. HANLEY TO FAMILY LAW SECTION OF AMERICAN BAR ASSOCIATION

In view of current controversies concerning the use of public funds in family-planning programs in the United States, the undersigned set forth the following opinions as a suggested basis for resolving these issues:

1. In a legitimate concern over public health, education, and poverty, the government may properly establish programs which permit citizens to exercise a free choice in matters of responsible parenthood in accordance with their moral standards.

2. In such programs, the government may properly give information and assistance concerning medically accepted forms of family planning, so long as human life and personal rights are safeguarded and no coercion or pressure is exerted against individual moral choice.

3. In such programs, the government should not imply a preference for any particular method of family planning.

4. While norms of private morality may have special dimensions so affecting the common good as to justify opposition to public programs, private moral judgments regarding methods of family planning do not provide a basis for opposition to government programs.

5. Although the use of public funds for purposes of family planning is not objectionable in principle, the manner in which such a program is implemented may pose issues requiring separate consideration.

These opinions are submitted as being morally justified and in accordance with the traditional Catholic position on birth control. These opinions are expressed out of a concern for civil liberty and freedom, and are based upon respect for the sincere consciences of our fellow citizens in this pluralistic society.

Father Hanley's statement was widely acclaimed by persons of all faiths as embodying the basic principles for the solution of this problem in a manner acceptable and fair to all. Newspapers throughout the country lauded it in editorials. Deeply moved by its fairness and reasonableness, Senator Ernest Gruening, chairman of the Senate subcommittee dealing with this problem (Senate Bill 1676), invited Father Hanley in behalf of the subcommittee to present his statement at a public hearing and thus make it a part of the official record.

This he did on August 24, 1965. Upon the completion of Father Hanley's statement Senator Gruening made the following comment: "I believe this is very satisfactory evidence of the potential coexistence of these views in which we can try to solve population problems without in any way injuring the sensibilities or religious convictions of any group, and in that way approaching this great problem, this overshadowing problem which really threatens the peace, health, and welfare of growing numbers of people all over the world, and has created, as you point out, a lot of new problems."

Testifying before the same Senate subcommittee was William E. Moran, Jr., dean of the School of Foreign Service of Georgetown University. He stressed the importance of communicating our knowledge to the people of the overpopulated nonindustrialized nations so they will be moved voluntarily to regulate population growth and increase production through the use of new methods. "We few," he said, "in the advanced industrialized countries cannot improve the lot of man throughout the world. We can at best help the two billion men and women in the world to improve their own lives."

Another witness appearing later before the subcommittee was Professor Donald N. Barrett, director of the Institute for Latin-American Population Research and professor of sociology at the University of Notre Dame. Stressing the need of responsible parenthood, he said: "Despite the arguments that man has removed himself through the technological revolution from his natural ecological checks and balances, I would insist that man will inevitably use his God-given powers of ratiocination to control population.

"This will not need the disasters foreseen so easily by users of demographic slide rules. The United Nations projections of six to seven billions by A.D. 2000 are realistic enough to encourage the development of policy . . . I would make clear that the basic principles stated before this subcommittee by the Rev. Dexter L. Hanley, S.J., last August 24 have my concurrence." The expression of his complete agreement with the principles set forth by Father Hanley is of especial interest because Dr. Barrett is a member of the Commission on Marriage, Family, and Births appointed by Pope Paul VI to advise him on these matters.

Voicing opposition to these principles was William B. Ball, general counsel for the Pennsylvania Catholic Conference. He condemned the use of public funds to support birth-control services and said "this is no place for government." He would have the government render no assistance whatsoever to the many people seeking help in regulating the number of their offspring.

At the conclusion of his testimony, Senator Gruening first pointed out that the government has been rendering aid in family planning since the mid-1930s. He then noted that the Declaration of Independence proclaimed that life, liberty, and the pursuit of happiness are basic objectives of the society that its framers visualized for America.

"Certainly," said the senator, "it is very clear in almost all the testimony we have had—and I think it is self-evident that a large element of human happiness is involved in this issue . . . that much unhappiness results from uncontrolled breeding, sickly children, too many children, broken families, husbands deserting their wives because they give up in despair."

When the sentiments expressed by Mr. Ball were reported to be the "official" view, many Catholic scholars throughout the country were considerably disturbed. The argument that the government was engaging in coercion by offering information and help in family planning solely to those who want such aid and in the manner desired, seemed to Catholic scholars generally not only fallacious but also an implicit attempt to impose a distinctive creedal viewpoint upon others. Virtually all Protestants and most Jews believe in the morality of medically approved birth-control methods. Furthermore their religious leaders affirm that in some circumstances it is their positive duty to use such methods.

Here, then, to the dismay and chagrin of Catholic scholars generally, was an attempt through political pressure to exclude the government from a field in which its services are approved by the vast majority of citizens of all faiths.

Thus the Gallup Poll of 1965 reported that in answer to the question, "Do you favor or oppose the distribution of birth-control information?", 80 per cent of Protestants answered in favor and only 12 per cent opposed; 60 per cent of Catholics answered in favor and only 28 per cent opposed; 84 per cent of all others answered in favor and but 14 per cent opposed.

Moreover a later Gallup Poll in October 1965 reported that 65 per cent approve federal aid for family-planning clinics, including 59 per cent of American Catholics. When asked whether they favored the United Nations' supplying information on all birth-control methods to people anywhere in the world who want it, 67 per cent of Catholics answered yes and but 24 per cent replied no.

For whom then was Mr. Ball speaking? Certainly not for Protestants or Jews, and not even for most Catholics. Involved here was no abstract matter of church doctrine, no religious dogma, no truth revealed in the holy Scriptures. It was solely a matter that called for a "prudential" judgment on the simple question: Isn't family planning, which affects so deeply the health, welfare, and happiness of millions of citizens, especially the poor, the downtrodden, and the underprivileged, a matter of legitimate concern for the government? Must the government, which concerns itself with so many phases of the citizen's life and welfare, be excluded from this most important aspect? Excluded even when its help is desperately needed and urgently sought?

The overwhelming majority of Catholics, like those of other faiths, refuse to believe this is of no concern to the government. They refuse to believe it even when their ecclesiastical leaders seek to exert political pressure to prevent the government from rendering such service. They find their true sentiments better expressed in the comment made by Senator Gruening at the close of Mr. Ball's testimony, which was previously quoted.

Deeply concerned over the misrepresentation of their profound convictions by those who were ostensibly speaking officially for them, Catholic scholars across the nation sought desperately to find some way to express their true sentiments. Some forty Catholic scholars met and formed the Catholic Committee on Population and Government Policy. They decided to run an ad in *The National Catholic Reporter, America,* and *Commonweal* to offer the opportunity to other Catholics to voice their support of the principles set forth by Father Hanley and the original group of fifty-six other scholars. They thought that perhaps a hundred signatures from other Catholic scholars might be secured.

To their pleasant surprise, in a short time the signatures of 517 streamed in from all parts of the country. It was significant that out of 522 responses, only five were negative. The signatures included persons from fifty-seven colleges and universities, twenty-one medical doctors, forty-five Catholic clergy, twenty-one nuns, and seventeen lawyers, including the deans of the law schools at three large universities. Scholars from every academic discipline—the humanities, social and political science, physical and natural sciences, and theology—are represented in the signatures, and they come from thirty-seven states.

Dr. William V. D'Antonio, chairman of the executive committee of the Catholic Committee on Population and Government Policy, appeared before the subcommittee on Manpower, Employment, and Poverty of the Senate committee on Labor and Public Welfare on May 10, 1966. "The executive committee of my group," he testified, "is composed of professors from Fordham, Georgetown, Harvard, Hunter, Pace, the University of Pennsylvania, and the University of Notre Dame. . . . Our involvement in the efforts to expand government action in the field of family planning stems from the deep impression which was made on us by the courageous statement presented by Rev. Dexter L. Hanley, S.J., of Georgetown University School of Law to the Family Law Section, American Bar Association, Miami, Florida, August 1965. . . .

"What we are asserting here," he said, "by my presence this morning and by the position taken by the signees and the executive committee of the Catholic Committee on Population and Government Policy, is our belief that action by the federal government in the field of family planning is well within the constitutional limits and seen by us as desirable social legislation. Most importantly, we would like to emphasize the fact that, in a pluralistic society, some legislation may be desirable even though it may not be in accord with the moral principles of a minority of the society's members.

"It seems clear in the present case that a vast majority of Americans approve of federal aid for family-planning clinics—65 per cent according to the Gallup Poll on October 1965. Furthermore, 59 per cent of American Catholics in this poll also approved of such aid. We stand with these majorities."

As one reviews the statement of the Catholic bishops, a few questions inevitably arise. First. Why the speed with which the statement was pushed through? On a matter of such importance can anyone imagine the Congress of the United States taking less than several weeks?

Would not the House of Representatives and the Senate appoint committees to investigate every phase of the question? Would they not invite representatives of various viewpoints to express their opinions at committee hearings? What would be the uproar throughout the nation if Congress did not proceed in this deliberate manner, giving ample time to all interested parties?

Yet the bishops did none of these. They pushed it through in a matter of seconds. This is all the more surprising since they knew that Catholic scholars—the impressive Hanley group and the still larger national Catholic Committee on Population and Government Policy—had publicly voiced their approval of the government providing assistance to those who wished it and in the manner which harmonized with the conscientious convictions of each recipient. It was public knowledge, too, that the Gallup Poll reported that 81 per cent of Catholics favored federal birth-control aid to married American women.

Second. The whole question of the morality of birth regulation by other than the unreliable rhythm method was at the time under general reconsideration and reappraisal by the Church. Top-notch theologians had publicly questioned the traditional line of reasoning. In scholarly journals they declared there was no substantial moral difference between the use of the rhythm method with its calendar, thermometer, and test tape and some other medically approved methods, which were simpler and more effective. Cardinals at the Council had urged that the Church reappraise its stand in the light of the findings of medical science and the conclusions of theologians.

As a result of these new and significant developments, Pope Paul VI had appointed a commission of numerous scholars to advise him. It has been widely reported that the majority favored the acceptance of the new and effective methods developed by medical science. In a remarkably frank interview with Alberto Cavallari, a representative of the Milan daily, *Corriere della Sera,* on October 19, 1965, the Pope acknowledged that the world was awaiting a decision from him but that he did not know what to say. More than a year later he declared that he had still reached no decision and that "the Church is in a state of pause and reflection" on this problem.

Why then, one wonders, did not the bishops reflect at their Washington meeting the state of pause and reflection in which the Church was officially at that time? While the old norms were to continue "for the present," as the Pope phrased it, it was evident that the old ruling was undergoing a searching reappraisal of unprecedented dimensions and that the overwhelming majority of Catholics were expecting a new decision that would reflect the new developments in both theology and science. Why, one wonders, was not this new posture of the Church reflected in some way in the bishops' action? Why was there not a long pause after the reading of the statement and a period of at least several days spent in deliberation and reflection?

Role of Laity

Third. Pope John XXIII, Pope Paul VI, and the Council had all stressed the new and important role which the laity were to play in the life and ministry of the Church. They were told that they were to help the Church henceforth not only with their material resources, as in the past, but also with their thought and experience especially in the fields of their competence. In what field do they have more experience than in dealing with the problem of spacing offspring in accordance with the conditions of their health and resources?

Furthermore, thousands of them are physicians, gynecologists, obstetricians, lawyers, judges, social workers, and experts in the social and political sciences. Isn't it strange that not one of this vast multitude was called in for consultation? Didn't they have something to contribute to the shaping of that "prudential judgment" which was to be expressed in the bishops' statement?

"Laymen," said John F. Donnelly, president of the National Council of Catholic Men, "should be consulted on policy statements made by the NCWC or the new organization (the renamed U. S. Catholic Conference). Consultation with laymen before policy statements by the U. S. bishops has been extremely seldom. At the moment, I can't think of a case."

Donnelly pointed out that an organization like NCCM is needed to enable the layman to know his own mind and to have the courage to speak it. It should have considerable autonomy and a means for close dialogue with a body of bishops, so that mutual understanding and trust can develop. "Repeated efforts," he reported, "have failed to achieve such a mechanism, so I have resigned, hoping that the bishops will realize that there is an unmet need."

If there is a house of lords for the bishops, should not there be a house of commons for representatives of the laity, when matters affecting their relations with their non-Catholic neighbors are involved? Isn't there an urgent need for a new structure in the Church that will enable the laity to express their thought in the fields of their competence, as

Vatican Council has asked them to do? Can anyone believe that the bishops would have issued the same statement if the competent Catholic scholars consulted by the U. S. Senate committees had been consulted by the bishops?

Fourth. The public image of the Church, created by the opposition of Catholic ecclesiastical authorities toward the efforts to extend aid to people seeking to regulate the number of their offspring, is an unfavorable one. It appears to be stubbornly obstructionist, with little or no concern for the agonizing difficulties of families struggling with this problem. John Duveen depicts that image in this book. Some years ago Theodore Gill did so in *The Christian Century.*

"With every will in the world," he wrote, "to help and lift and heal mankind, the Church's obduracy on birth control finally dooms all its own remedial efforts as well as the nation's best ambitions. So far the Church's thinkers show no will to do anything but let the world smash itself on Rome's tenacious legalisms." That is the all too common public image of the Church, and it can be changed only when the Church co-operates *constructively* with other churches, foundations, and public authorities in dealing with this problem on the city, county, state, national, and international planes. Is the bishops' statement likely to change that public image?

These are some of the questions which inevitably arise when one considers the bishops' statement on "The Government and Birth Control" and the strange and incomprehensible manner in which it was pushed through without a single word of inquiry, appraisal, or discussion.

13

CHURCHES SPEAK UP

by John A. O'Brien

In a society with many different religious faiths, it is of the utmost importance that no one group seek to impose its distinctive dogmatic or moral creed upon others. There is a subtle temptation to do this in localities where one group is particularly numerous and hence politically powerful. Where a group succumbs to this temptation, strife, bitterness, and ultimately court action result.

Probably no country has a greater variety of religious denominations than the United States, whose citizens stem from all nations. More than 250 different denominations were listed in the last federal religious census. Virtually every religious creed with an appreciable membership anywhere in the Old World is likely to have some of its adherents here. Hence it is necessary for all citizens to recognize this great variety of religious faiths and to respect the constitutional rights of all citizens to practice their faiths without let or hindrance.

While abstract religious dogmas are no longer likely to precipitate strife, as they did in the days of the early colonists, differences in moral codes tend to do so. This is true particularly in regard to birth control, and especially when the funds of the government or of the community chest are sought to implement its practice by a method not in harmony with the moral beliefs of others.

Until the second quarter of the twentieth century all religious denominations condemned contraception as immoral. Due largely to the crusading activities of Anthony Comstock, the U. S. Congress in 1873 enacted a statute excluding contraceptives and information about their use from the mails on the grounds of obscenity. Numerous states followed suit and passed laws banning the sale and distribution of contraceptives, thus hindering the acceptance of birth control by the general public.

One of the first to crusade against such legislation was Margaret Sanger, a New York nurse. In 1912 she began lecturing against it and two years later founded a monthly magazine, *The Woman Rebel.* She was arrested and indicted under the Comstock law. She escaped to Europe, and the following year her husband was jailed for a short term for handing out a copy of her pamphlet on *Family Limitation.*

Returning to the United States, Mrs. Sanger opened on October 16, 1916, the first Birth Control Clinic in the United States in Brooklyn. This was closed by the police, and Mrs. Sanger and her sister were given thirty-day jail sentences. Spurred on, however, by her knowledge of the sufferings of many women from too frequent pregnancies, Mrs. Sanger continued her work and founded the National Birth Control League and the publication, *Birth Control Review.*

She helped organize national and international conferences, and in 1921 the New York Birth Control Clinical Research Bureau opened. This was raided by police in 1929 and its director arrested. But as public opinion was now beginning to favor birth control, the director was released and the clinic was permitted to continue its work. What seems to have caused the tide of public opinion to begin to turn in favor of birth control was the recommendation in 1925 by the gynecological section of the American Medical Association that the law be modified to permit physicians to give contraceptive advice.

In March 1931, the Federal Council of Churches of Christ in America endorsed contraceptive methods of birth control by a vote of 24 to 4. In a statement on this subject the council declared: "The public has a right to expect guidance from the church on the moral aspects of birth control. As to the necessity for some form of effective control of the size of the family and spacing of children, and consequently of control of conception, there can be no question. It is recognized by all churches and physicians. There is general agreement that sex union between husbands and wives as an expression of mutual affection without relation to procreation is right. This is recognized by the Scriptures, by all branches of the Christian church, by social and medical science, and by the good sense and idealism of mankind."

Since the action of the Federal Council in 1931, virtually every Protestant denomination has issued its own statement endorsing medically prescribed methods of birth control and even affirming the duty of its members in certain circumstances to use such methods. Further support came from the American Neurological Association, the Eugenics Society, and the Central Conference of Rabbis. In 1936 a ruling of the District Court, that contraceptives imported for a lawful purpose did not come within the restrictions of federal law, was upheld by the Court of Appeals. The following year the American Medical Association unanimously agreed to accept birth control "as an integral part of medical practice and education."

In 1958 the Lambeth Conference of the Anglican Church voiced unanimous approval of contraception in the following terms: "The Conference believes that the responsibility for deciding upon the number and frequency of children has been laid by God upon the consciences of parents everywhere: that this planning, in such ways as are mutually acceptable to husband and wife in Christian conscience, is a right and important factor in Christian family life and should be the result of positive choice before God. Such responsible parenthood, built on obedience to all the duties of marriage, requires a wise stewardship of the resources and abilities of the family as well as a thoughtful consideration of the varying population needs and problems of society and the claims of future generations."

What had greatly influenced public opinion and prepared it for the acceptance of contraception were chiefly two factors. The first was the discovery by medical science of simple, effective, and harmless methods, such as the pill and the intrauterine device for the regulation of pregnancy. The second was the marked increase in population with indications that the increase in births was exceeding the increase in food supplies, especially in the developing countries.

Reflecting the widespread view that it is well to use the new findings of medical science to regulate conception, Joseph Fletcher wrote in

Morals and Medicine in 1954: "With the medical technology of contraception, parenthood and birth control become matters of moral responsibility, of intelligent choice. We are able to control our fertility. No longer do we have to choose between reproduction and continence. Sex is no longer a helpless submission to biological consequences. Nor is the only alternative a denial of sexual love, either *in toto* or according to lunar calculations in a sophisticated and doubtful rhythm mathematics. When such calculations enter in, the spontaneity of love goes out. Rhythm is a denial of freedom; it offers only an alternation of necessities, not a method of true control."

Similar is the view expressed in 1958 by Dr. Gustafson, president of the New York Conference of the Augustana Lutheran Church: "An unrestrained production of children without realistic regard to God-given responsibilities involved in bringing them up in the discipline and instruction of the Lord may be as sinful and as selfish an indulgence of the lusts of the flesh as is the complete avoidance of parenthood."

With the acceptance of birth control by the general public, the statutes of various states banning the sale of contraceptives became more honored in the breach than in the observance. Moreover, since the Roman Catholic Church was left virtually isolated among Christian denominations in condemning artificial birth control, such statutes became increasingly open to the charge of violating the separation of Church and state guaranteed by the first amendment. It could also be contended that the statutes interfered with religious freedom.

Such in fact was the contention made by three Protestant ministers—an Episcopalian, a Methodist, and a Lutheran—on May 4, 1959, in asking the Superior Court for a ruling on the Connecticut statute. The clergymen maintained that the law banning dissemination of birth-control advice deprived them of their "liberty, freedom of speech, and right to freely practice their religions." They asserted that they were "bound by the teachings of our Churches and our own religious beliefs to counsel parishioners on the use of contraceptive devices and to advise them and to counsel to use same and to give advice in premarital counseling."

This is important for Roman Catholics to remember. Keenly aware of the condemnation of contraception by their own Church, there is a tendency, perhaps unconscious, of Catholics to impose their viewpoint on others. They seem to forget that by so doing they are violating the rights of others both to follow their own conscience and to practice their own religions. Hence it was that the Connecticut statute was declared unconstitutional. No longer can the Roman Catholic argue that he has the sanction and support of the civil law behind him in his opposition to contraceptive birth control.

In official statements Protestant churches and Jewish organizations have affirmed their belief in the morality of contraception and even the duty in many circumstances to practice it. They stress the responsibility of parenthood and the duty of not bringing into existence children for whom they cannot make proper provision. Contraception is virtually the only effective way of doing this, they point out, without in effect destroying the chief means of fostering love and deepening the union of husband and wife.

Before me are the official statements of many Protestant denominations, too numerous and lengthy to be quoted in their entirety. Hence I shall cite but a key sentence or so from the official statements of some of the larger ones.

The United Presbyterian Church in the United States at the 174th and 175th General Assemblies in 1962 and 1963 declared: "We have the right and responsibility, not only to engage in family planning, but also to choose the appropriate means . . . Care must be exercised . . . so that [new products] will be used for . . . conception control and not . . . destruction of life . . . No patient in a tax-supported agency should be denied treatment . . . that is in accord with sound medical advice . . . but [none should] be required to accept treatment . . . contrary to the teaching of his faith."

The Protestant Episcopal Church in the U. S. General Conventions, 1961 and 1964 stated: "Family planning, in such ways as are mutually acceptable to husband and wife in Christian conscience, and secure from the corruptions of sensuality and selfishness, is a right and important factor in Christian family life . . . Members of the Church [are urged] to work . . . for adequate resources for family planning, including public health and welfare agencies."

The Methodist Church, General Conference, 1964, declared that "planned parenthood, practiced with respect for human life, fulfills rather than violates the will of God. It is the duty of each married couple prayerfully and responsibly to seek parenthood, avert it, or defer it, in accordance with the best expression of their Christian love."

The Baptist Church, American Baptist Convention, 1963, declared: "We urge: Acceptance of the principle that parents have the right [of] responsible family planning . . . Greatly increased private and government support of medical research to speed development of safe, reliable, inexpensive, and acceptable methods of birth control . . . Dissemination by the government of the United States . . . of information and equipment needed for family limitation."

The Lutheran Church in America, Conventions 1956, 1964, asserted: "Husband and wife are called to exercise the power of procreation responsibly before God. This implies planning their parenthood in accordance with their ability to provide for their children and carefully nurture them in fullness of Christian faith and life."

The Unitarian-Universalist Church, Unitarian Universalist Association, 1962, stated: "We urge: The Congress . . . to pass legislation [to] support . . . intensive research . . . to discover inexpensive, harmless, and effective birth-control methods, and permitting the dissemination of . . . information to those nations which request [it. We urge] local, state, federal governments . . . [to] remove restrictions [on] the responsible distribution of . . . information and devices."

The Society of Friends, Philadelphia Yearly Meeting, 1962, said: "We endorse planned parenthood and hope that qualified professional advice may be given to those seeking it, concerning both contraception and the promotion of fertility when that is the need."

The United Church of Christ, comprising the Congregational Christian Church and the Evangelical and Reformed Church, in 1960 declared: "Responsible family planning is today a clear moral duty . . . public law and public institutions should sanction the distribution . . . of reliable information and contraceptive devices. Laws which forbid doctors, social workers, and ministers to provide such information and service are infringements of the rights of free citizens . . . Any hospital which receives public funds should permit doctors to provide all services they consider necessary."

The Jewish Rabbinic Assembly in 1961 stated: "There is precedent in Jewish law for sanctioning birth control . . . The vocation of parenthood fulfills its God-endowed mission when it is rendered consistent with the requisites of the life and health of all the constituent members of the family."

The American Jewish Congress on November 7, 1965, declared: "We call upon our government to utilize the best available medical knowledge and resources towards a voluntary program of family limitation and planning by making contraceptive birth-control information and materials available to those who need it most and can afford it least, through the Office of Economic Opportunity and other federal, state, and local governmental agencies."

The Union of American Hebrew Congregations speaking for Reformed Judaism in 1959 stated: "We are concerned with restrictions placed upon the availability of information and medical assistance in the planning of families. We fully recognize the right of all persons, for religious reasons or otherwise, to abstain from or to practice birth control as they see fit. However, the failure of large sections of our population to plan their families effectively is due neither to conscience nor to free choice, but rather to legal and official obstacles imposed upon many Americans with the result of depriving them of knowledge and medical assistance in this field. This dearth of information and assistance most directly affects those families which, for lack of financial and educational resources, have the greatest need. Many social problems, including desertion, nonsupport of families, illegitimacy, high divorce rates, mental and emotional instability, may be the result in part of ineffectual birth-control practices in our society.

"When government responds to the theological beliefs of any religious group by interfering with the dissemination of birth-control information to all who desire it, such interference represents an improper imposition of such religious beliefs upon the community at large. Therefore, be it resolved that:

"1. We favor the elimination of all restrictions and prohibitions against the dissemination of birth-control information and the rendering of birth-control assistance by qualified physicians, clinics, and hospitals.

"2. We favor the wider dissemination of birth-control information and medical assistance, both by private groups, such as the Planned

Parenthood Association, and health agencies of local, state, and the federal government as a vital service to be rendered in the field of public health."

Reflecting the thought, convictions, and faith of virtually all the Protestant churches in the United States is the carefully formulated and detailed statement of the National Council of Churches, which merits quoting in full.

STATEMENT OF THE NATIONAL COUNCIL OF CHURCHES OF CHRIST IN THE
UNITED STATES OF AMERICA ON RESPONSIBLE PARENTHOOD,
FEBRUARY 23, 1961

In recent decades, advances in medical science have affected marriage and family life in at least two important ways. Because of dramatic reductions in death rates, children generally have a far brighter chance to live to maturity; indeed, the persistence of large family patterns in many societies causes new and dangerous pressures upon presently inadequate means of subsistence. On the other hand, new medical knowledge of human reproduction increases the means available or potentially available to parents for regulating their fertility.

In the altered circumstances of today, how is the Christian doctrine of parenthood to be made relevant to the needs of husbands and wives? Without attempting to restate the full range of parental duties, we advance certain considerations bearing on the control of procreation within the marriage bond. The concept of responsible parenthood is considered in relation to the ends of marriage, the reasons for family planning, the methods of family planning, and the task of society.

Genuine marriage, in the biblical view, is a union whereby husband and wife become "one flesh" (Genesis 2:24, Mark 10:8, Ephesians 5:31). Such a union embodies a covenant, a commitment to a dedicated common life. True marriage, however, is more than a human achievement. It has a "given" quality, expressed in the words of Jesus: "What . . . God has joined together" (Mark 10:9). Hence it is a mystery according to St. Paul which symbolizes the union of Christ and His Church (Ephesians 5:32) and is, in turn, illumined by this perfect union.

Since holy matrimony involves an occasion of God's grace, it is clear that the first duty of husband and wife is to nourish and care for the gift which God has given. This task is described in Christian traditions in terms of sanctification and mutual perfection. These emphasize the fundamentally spiritual character of the basic purpose of marriage, which can be served through parenthood, companionship, and vocation:

1. Parenthood is a divinely ordained purpose of marriage for the embodiment and completion of the "one flesh" union, for the care and nurture of children, for building the home as a true community of persons, and for the peopling of the earth (Genesis 1:28). It is participation in God's continuing creation, which calls for awe, gratitude, and a sense of high responsibility.

2. Mutual love and companionship, rooted in the need of husband and wife for each other (Genesis 2:18), have also been ordained of God for the welfare and perfection of the "one flesh" union and for broader aspects of the sharing of life. Christians differ in regard to sanctions for the sexual expression of marital companionship, though most of our churches hold such expression right and necessary within the marriage bond, independently of procreation. All agree that Christian marriage should be free from sensuality and selfish indulgence, and that mutually accepted periods of continence can be of value in a common life of Christian discipline.

3. Vocation, or the service of the couple in society, is another high purpose through which "the two become one." It normally includes parenthood and family life as major elements, but can assert a separate or even conflicting claim on conscience. Just as vocation may enjoin celibacy upon those to whom the gift is given (Matthew 19:11), so the calling of the couple may in certain circumstances enjoin family limitation.

Responsible parenthood, in the first instance, means to weigh the claims of procreation in relation to the total purposes of the marriage and the situation of the family in society. For most couples, the new knowledge of human reproduction and of means to avert conception affects ethical decisions regarding parenthood. But the responsibility, to be exercised in prayer and trust, has deeper roots.

Within the purposes of marriage ordained by God, there are a number of considerations concerning parenthood which need to be taken into account in trying to determine the number and frequency of pregnancies. These include:

1. The right of the child to be wanted, loved, cared for, educated and trained in the "discipline and instruction of the Lord" (Ephesians 6:4). The rights of existing children to parental care have a proper claim.

2. The prospects for health of a future child, if medical and eugenic evidence seem negatively conclusive.

3. The health and welfare of the mother-wife, and the need for the spacing of children to safeguard them.

4. The social situation, when rapid population growth places dangerous pressures on the means of livelihood and endangers the social order.

Reasons such as these enter into the calculations of responsible parenthood. At the same time, parents need to remember that having children is a venture in faith, requiring a measure of courage and confidence in God's goodness. Too cautious a reckoning of the costs may be as great an error as failure to lift the God-given power of procreation to the level of ethical decision.

Christians are agreed that the limitation of procreation may be right and proper for parents under certain conditions, but differences arise in regard to circumstances and methods. The Orthodox Church follows the traditional teaching which sanctions marital abstinence as the means of family planning. Most of the Protestant churches hold contraception and periodic continence to be morally right when the motives are right.

They believe that couples are free to use the gifts of science for conscientious family limitation, provided the means are mutually acceptable, noninjurious to health, and appropriate to the degree of effectiveness required in the specific situation. Periodic continence (the rhythm method) is suitable for some couples, but is not inherently superior from a moral point of view. The general Protestant conviction is that motives, rather than methods, form the primary moral issue, provided the methods are limited to the prevention of conception.

Protestant Christians are agreed on condemning abortion or any method which destroys human life, except when the health or life of the mother is at stake. The destruction of life already begun cannot be condoned as a method of family limitation. The ethical complexities involved in the practice of abortion related to abnormal circumstances need additional study by Christian scholars.

Another approach to family limitation is voluntary sterilization. Because medical science cannot guarantee that the procedure is reversible it presents the Christian conscience with special problems. Responsible parenthood is seen by many as a day-to day-process of decision making which sterilization may negate.

On the other hand, where reasons of health or the obligations of parenthood argue for the use of the most effective means of family limitation, sterilization represents one sure method now available. Recognizing the dilemmas confronting Christian doctors and parents, particularly in some of the poorer societies where realistic alternatives seem to be lacking, we are constrained to point out the hazards in sterilization, and to stress the possibility of its use only after the most thoughtful consideration of all the factors involved. Additional study of these factors and of the moral issues entailed needs to be undertaken by Christian scholars.

While responsible parenthood is the moral obligation of husband and wife, the concept has implications for society also to assist parents in the exercise of their duty. In addition to the educational and social services called for to help equip children for their fullest development and contribution to society, there are services due married couples. For most couples, family planning requires access to appropriate medical information and counsel.

Legal prohibitions against impartation of such information and counsel violate the civil and religious liberties of all citizens, including Protestants. Their right to means they approve in conscience does not infringe the right of others to refrain from using such means. Legislation or institutional practices that impair the exercise of moral and professional responsibilities of family-serving professions should be opposed.

As Christians and citizens in a world society, we also have the responsibility to help our fellow men overseas. Public-health programs in economically less developed countries, often with substantial assistance from our government, have helped to create new population pressures. Therefore, at the request of people in other countries, we believe our government and voluntary agencies have a duty to assist with various measures to alleviate population pressures and to extend family planning.

Private agencies have an important role to play, but the scope of the population problem internationally vastly exceeds their resources. Christian responsibility indicates that, when requested by other governments, governmental and intergovernmental aid for family planning should be given favorable consideration as part of a wise and dedicated effort to advance in the underprivileged regions of the earth the essential material conditions conducive to human dignity, freedom, justice, and peace.

There is little doubt that the statement of the National Council of Churches reflects the general view of the overwhelming majority not only of Protestants and Jews but also of the American people with no definite church affiliation. It doubtless reflects also the views of the vast majority of the people of the world today. Confronted with soaring population that is outracing the supply of food, an ever-increasing number of the nations are appealing for help.

On December 10, 1966, the anniversary of the United Nations Declaration of Human Rights, the heads of state of Colombia, Finland, India, Malaysia, the Republic of Korea, Singapore, Sweden, Tunisia, the United Arab Republic, Yugoslavia, Morocco, and Nepal presented to U Thant, secretary-general of the United Nations, the following significant statement.

STATEMENT OF TWELVE NATIONS ON FAMILY PLANNING
AND HUMAN RIGHTS

The peace of the world is of paramount importance to the community of nations, and our governments are devoting their best efforts to improving the prospects for peace in this and succeeding generations. But another great problem threatens the world—a problem less visible but no less immediate. That is the problem of unplanned population growth.

It took mankind all of recorded time until the middle of the last century to achieve a population of one billion. Yet it took less than a hundred years to add the second billion, and only thirty years to add the third. At today's rate of increase, there will be four billion people by 1975 and nearly seven billion by the year 2000. This unprecedented increase presents us with a situation unique in human affairs and a problem that grows more urgent with each passing day.

The numbers themselves are striking, but their implications are of far greater significance. Too rapid population growth seriously hampers efforts to raise living standards, to further education, to improve health and sanitation, to provide better housing and transportation, to forward cultural and recreational opportunities—and even in some countries to assure sufficient food. In short, the human aspiration, common to men everywhere, to live a better life is being frustrated and jeopardized.

As heads of governments actively concerned with the population problem, we share these convictions:

We believe that the population problem must be recognized as a principal element in long-range national planning if governments are to achieve their economic goals and fulfill the aspirations of their people.

We believe that the great majority of parents desire to have the knowledge and the means to plan their families; that the opportunity to decide the number and spacing of children is a basic human right.

We believe that lasting and meaningful peace will depend to a considerable measure upon how the challenge of population growth is met.

We believe the objective of family planning is the enrichment of human life, not its restriction; that family planning, by assuring greater opportunity to each person frees man to attain his individual dignity and reach his full potential.

Recognizing that family planning is in the vital interest of both the nation and the family, we earnestly hope that leaders around the world will share our views and join with us in this great challenge for the well-being and happiness of people everywhere.

STATEMENT OF U THANT ON POPULATION

Acknowledging the receipt of the statement from the leaders of the twelve nations, the secretary-general issued the following statement.

Today I have received a declaration on population growth and human dignity and welfare signed by the heads of state of Colombia,

Finland, India, Malaysia, the Republic of Korea, Singapore, Sweden, Tunisia, the United Arab Republic, Yugoslavia, Morocco, and Nepal. I have been requested to circulate this statement in connection with Human Rights Day, the celebration of the anniversary of the United Nations Declaration of Human Rights, and it seems to me appropriate to do so inasmuch as freedom from hunger, the right to medical services, and the right to education are already considered to be basic human rights.

Accordingly I take this occasion to emphasize that population growth is not only an important factor in the rate at which nations can attain their economic goals, but that the size of the family is a fundamental human problem which must be based on the decisions of responsible parents concerned with the dignity and well-being of their children.

In my view, we must accord the parents' right to determine the numbers of their children a place of importance at this moment in man's history. For, as one of the consequences of backwardness, rates of population growth are very much higher in the poor two thirds of the world than they are among the more privileged countries, and it is being increasingly realized that, over the two or three decades immediately ahead, when present world-wide efforts to raise food production will not have yielded the fullest results, the problem of growing food shortage cannot be solved without in many cases a simultaneous effort to moderate population growth.

We recognize and fully respect the problems of faith and conscience which many still face in relation to the means designed to achieve this objective. But on this Human Rights Day, I feel bound to call attention to a declaration expressing concern with the quality of human life as well as with the number of human beings on earth.

14

U. S. POLICIES AND OBJECTIVES

by Ellen Winston

Dr. Ellen Winston heads the new Welfare Administration
in the Department of Health, Education, and Welfare,
which includes the Bureau of Family Services, Children's
Bureau, Office of Juvenile Delinquency and Youth Development, and Cuban Refugee Program.

In discussing family planning, I shall explore an aspect of our national
health and social needs which has been shrouded far too long in taboos
and controversy. Only a few years ago, I could not have treated this
subject with the candor it deserves.

But now, fortunately, the climate has changed and the opportunities
for service through the United States Department of Health, Education, and Welfare are greatly increased. The challenge we face today
is in part one which we have helped to create. The thrust of our challenge is seen most acutely as we look about the world today, particularly to the new and developing nations. In these less-developed lands,
unbridled population growth is now outstripping new and hard-won
social and economic gains.

I need not dwell here at length on the world's population statistics.

They tell their own story dramatically. At the start of the Christian era there were some 250 million people on earth. It took almost 1700 years for the world's population to double, then 200 years to double again, and then only 100 years to double once more. At the present rate of increase, it will double again in just thirty-five years—from three billion people today to six billion by the end of this century.

What concerns us, and profoundly, is not only the recording of increased numbers but the record of unmet needs in health, in education, in social welfare, in the hope of human fulfillment. Internationally, we are coming to recognize that the gravest consequences face the world because of the growing gap between the rich and poor nations. There is now growing awareness in many of these nations of the urgency of family-planning programs.

Now we are facing up to the fact that population problems clearly concern us at home, that the barrier of silence about family planning has contributed in our own country to the gap between affluence and poverty, between hope and despair. The right of all our people to have access to information about this deeply human concern has been abridged too long.

We are now recognizing our responsibility to remove this barrier of silence. We recognize that family planning can no longer remain the quiet privilege of most of us, that to deny access to information and services to any of us is in itself a deprivation. We are conscious of our new opportunities to expand family-planning programs through a partnership of private and public efforts, with the federal resources at hand to support these programs, and with the implications of these programs for family and community health.

Family planning as a concern of the federal government has a remarkably short history. A decade ago, programs and information on family planning were a province reserved almost exclusively for voluntary groups and private citizens. Sharp controversy over the government's role in this sensitive area was voiced—when voices were heard —in both public discussion and in the legislative and executive councils of government.

In our state governments, as in Washington, activities in this field were inhibited because of the fear of religious and political opposition. In a number of states, legal barriers also stood in the way. It was only in 1965, for example, that the United States Supreme Court declared unconstitutional a state law in Connecticut which prohibited physicians or hospitals from giving information about or dispensing contraceptive devices. In May 1966, Massachusetts became the last state to repeal its anticontraceptive law.

In recent years a major change has been taking place in public thinking and public policy toward family planning. It has been set in motion by many factors: our massive population shift to urban communities, with its attendant problems of overcrowding; our technological revolution, with its increasingly higher premium on advanced training and skills for employment; the lag between the findings of medical research and the making of these findings broadly available.

These factors, among others, led to a growing desire of families to limit their size and thus raise the expectations for the health, education, and welfare of their children. The desire to strengthen the integrity of the family and to develop each individual to his greatest potential has been, of course, deeply rooted in our culture. It is this traditional concern for the health and well-being of the family that has now found full expression in federal policy.

This policy is firmly based on the principle that family planning is a matter of individual, personal decision. It holds that information should be widely available upon which these individual decisions may be based. President Johnson stated the principle clearly in 1966 in his Message to Congress on Health and Education when he said: "We have a growing concern to foster the integrity of the family, and the opportunity for each child. It is essential that all families have access to information and services that will allow freedom to choose the number and spacing of their children within the dictates of individual conscience."

It is interesting to compare this statement of the President's with a letter written in 1941 by Surgeon General Thomas Parran. Dr. Parran said then, in response to an inquiry: "It is the policy of the Public Health Service to co-operate with the health departments of the various states in the programs which they decide are in the best interests . . . of the people whom they serve. Should a state department of health decide on its own initiative to undertake a child spacing program, . . .

the Public Health Service would give the proposal the same consideration as would be given to any other proposal in connection with the health program of the state."

On the surface, the two statements appear to be quite close together. The critical difference lies in the forthrightness of the President's declaration that society as a whole is deeply concerned with the problem and that resolving it is a broad and essential responsibility. This open approach to the problem now permits and encourages our forthright efforts. We have crossed an important threshold.

This threshold, of course, was not crossed suddenly. President Johnson's statement to the Congress was one of a series of public declarations over the past few years by the President and other public officials. The Senate has been gathering an impressive body of testimony from many expert witnesses during hearings on a family-planning bill introduced last year by Senator Ernest Gruening of Alaska, who has performed an outstanding public service through these hearings. Assistance to other nations concerned with population problems has become an accepted and important part of our program of foreign assistance.

Meanwhile, we in the Department of Health, Education, and Welfare have been stepping up our activities to respond to this concern of our society and to carry out the President's policy statements. Secretary Gardner is providing vigorous leadership for the department's activities in family planning and population problems—activities that will be carried out through the Children's Bureau and the Bureau of Family Services in the Welfare Administration, the Public Health Service, and the Office of Education.

In January 1966, the secretary established, for the first time, a departmental policy on family planning. In a memorandum to the heads of operating agencies, he defined our policy on population dynamics, fertility, sterility, and family planning in these words: "The policy of this department is to conduct and support programs of basic and applied research on the above topics; to conduct and support training programs; to collect and make available such data as may be necessary; to support, on request, health programs making family-planning information and services available; and to provide family-planning information and services, on request, to individuals who receive health services from operating agencies of the department.

"The objectives of the departmental policy are to improve the health of the people, to strengthen the integrity of the family, and to provide families the freedom of choice to determine the spacing of their children and the size of their families. Programs conducted or supported by the department shall guarantee freedom from coercion or pressure of mind or conscience. There shall be freedom of choice of method so that individuals can choose in accordance with the dictates of their consciences. The department will make known to state and local agencies that funds are available for programs of the sort described above, but it will bring no pressure upon them to participate in such programs.

"Each agency shall assure the effective carrying out of this policy, the regular evaluation of programs, and the reporting of information on programs to this office. The Assistant Secretary for Health and Scientific Affairs will serve as the focal point for departmental policy and program co-ordination; will review and evaluate policies and programs; will conduct liaison with other departments; and will co-operate with interested public and private groups."

The implications of this policy statement are clear. It emphasizes that the department is increasing its efforts and its programs, but that ultimate success will depend not upon what we do in Washington but upon the initiative in our states and communities to make full use of the resources at hand. There will be no pressure or coercion to employ these resources. But every effort will be made to help states and localities, at their request, to develop truly effective family-planning programs.

One way to define how we can help in these efforts is to describe the machinery of the agencies and bureaus of our department which are concerned with family planning and the various acts of Congress which underwrite their activities. At the outset, however, I should like to frame our perspective in terms of the people we are seeking to help, rather than the machinery that makes help possible. The federal programs involving family planning offer a wide range of support, but they become a cohesive whole only as they are shaped and carried out in communities.

These programs involve the support and stimulus of family planning through services and information, through training family-planning personnel, and through research. But of all these activities, the first and most commanding assignment is to reach people and to estab-

lish effective contact. A study by Frederick S. Jaffe, vice-president of
Planned Parenthood-World Population, has revealed some interesting
facts in this regard.[1] He found that, in any given area, there are four
potential groups, the first group being the least expensive and the
fourth most expensive.

The first group comes to a clinic merely because it has opened its
doors and the facilities are available. Only a minimal information program is involved.

The second group, slightly more expensive to serve, consists of those
who can be reached only through the establishment of neighborhood
clinics, located more or less in the heart of impoverished communities.

Third, there is a group that requires a more intensive educational
program. For this group, the cost of the educational program must
be added to the cost of the medical service.

The fourth group consists of persons who will come into the clinic
only if extensive home visiting, group counseling, and discussion techniques are used. This group appears to be the most expensive for
this reason, even if the home visitors employed are low-income non-
professionals hired at minimum salaries.

By distinguishing these four groups, Jaffe has highlighted the important problem we face today in family planning and many other
health and social services. In the United States, we have already built
a basic structure for public health and public welfare and for the de-
livery of medical-care services. Our present problem is to extend its
reach to improve its quality and effectiveness in family planning.

We know the audience we should be reaching and have thus far
failed to reach: the mothers who see no doctors or nurses, or who visit
a clinic only when the baby is due; the mothers whose health is at
hazard from pregnancies; mothers who are denied access to services
for any reasons. Until we reach these people, we are defaulting on a
basic responsibility.

It is often maintained that the poor are "unmotivated" to take advantage of services which they need and would benefit from. Yet, in
studying family planning, Jaffe has found that the poor, both white
and Negro, "show considerable readiness to respond to this service."

[1] Frederick S. Jaffe, "Financing Family Planning Services," *American Journal of
Public Health*, Vol. 56, No. 6, June 1966, pp. 912–17.

He reports that "Negro parents in all socioeconomic groups (except the few now living on southern farms) express a consistent desire for *smaller families than do whites.*"

"Far from revealing disintegration and unrelieved pathology," Jaffe states, "current trends in Negro fertility attitudes and behavior suggest a substantial reservoir of aspiration and indeed of strength on which positive service programs for impoverished Negro families can be based. . . . The expressed and demonstrated readiness of the Negro poor for fertility control is but one aspect of a readiness for a wide variety of measures aimed at improving mobility, and suggests that the response will be considerable to genuine services which are properly organized and delivered.

"The task," he concludes, "is to use our intelligence, imagination, and affluence to restructure existing service systems—health, welfare, education, and so forth—in order to fulfill these hopes and not thwart them."[2]

The problem of developing and maintaining effective contact is thus one of our critical tasks in family planning, as in other areas. Resources to support these efforts are at hand. Federal assistance for family planning is now provided through a broad variety of grants for health and welfare. Our challenge is to give them the essential focus. The major departmental support for family-planning services is through the Children's Bureau of the Welfare Administration, which provides formula grants to state health departments and project grants to state and local health departments.

State and local health departments are using the Maternal and Child Health formula grants, authorized under Title V of the Social Security Act, to provide the broad base of maternal and child health services so essential for family-planning programs. An increasing number of states are using these funds to add family-planning services to the spectrum of other services made available through these formula grants.

Another program administered by the Children's Bureau provides project grants to state and local health departments to meet up to 75 per cent of the costs of programs of comprehensive maternity care for women living in low-income areas. The authorization for this program

[2] Adelaide Cromwell Hill and Frederick S. Jaffe, "Negro Fertility and Family Size Preferences: Implications for Programming of Health and Social Services," *The Negro American.* Boston: Houghton Mifflin, 1966, pp. 205–24.

is thirty million dollars for the 1966 fiscal year. Fifty-one projects have been approved, over two thirds of which are in major cities. Nearly all of these projects include family-planning services.

As a result of the rapidly growing interest in family planning, an increasing number of state and local health departments are now providing family-planning services. More than forty states are now providing family-planning services in some parts of the state. Two years ago the number was thirteen. Approximately three million dollars of maternal and child health funds are being used this year specifically for family-planning services. Next year, we expect this amount to increase to about five million dollars. These figures do not include the cost of the medical examinations which accompany the provision of these services.

The Maternity and Infant Care Projects are making family-planning services available to an increasing number of women in low-income families who have never before had access to these services. In some cities it was this program that enabled local agencies to change their policies and to include family-planning services in tax-supported programs.

Through the Bureau of Family Services of the Welfare Administration, the department also assists in family planning by supporting state medical-care programs under public-assistance provisions of the Social Security Act. Federal matching funds are available in state-assistance programs to hire personnel for family-planning programs and to provide services, drugs, supplies, and transportation. The Bureau of Family Services, whose participation in this field has increased considerably in recent months, is actively working with state public welfare agencies that wish to initiate or expand support for family-planning programs.

Title XIX, a major amendment to the Social Security Act enacted last year, will serve as a further impetus to the development of these programs in states where there have been limited programs in the past. Title XIX provides federal funds to states for medical services to individuals and families whose income and resources are insufficient to meet the costs of necessary medical expenses. Funds available to the states under this title can be used to develop family-planning services as part of a state's effort to provide comprehensive health services.

The significance of this new medical-assistance program is that states will be able to develop programs of comprehensive high-quality medical care for those on public assistance as well as others who are medically needy. Federally approved plans are now in operation in twenty-five states, Puerto Rico, and the Virgin Islands. Illinois was among the first of the states to operate under an approved plan. Other states in this region that now have approved programs are Michigan, Ohio, and Wisconsin.

In addition to the Welfare Administration's programs, other assistance for family-planning services is available through the Public Health Service, which administers general health grants to states for state and local public health purposes. These general grants are designed to give financial support for and to stimulate the development of adequate state and local programs to promote the nation's health. These programs should be markedly strengthened now that Congress, as one of its final actions before adjournment, passed the Partnership for Health Act. This legislation will give the states more flexibility and funds to develop public-health programs at the state and local level.

In only one respect does the department itself provide direct family-planning services. These are offered through the Public Health Service to specific beneficiaries who receive federal health care, among whom are American Indians, Alaska natives, and dependents of the uniformed services.

While there are several sources of federal support, the turning point in family planning is the resolution of states and communities to bring these services to their citizens. Much of value can be learned from the experience of states and localities which already have progressive family-planning programs.

One of the best examples of a successful local program is to be found in Mecklenburg County, North Carolina. A family-planning clinic, under health department auspices, has been operating there for almost thirty years, but it is only within the past five years that its services have reached many of the seriously deprived families who receive public assistance. The change came about when the director of the local public welfare department took the initiative in bringing together key personnel from the public health and public welfare agencies and worked out a program for making family-planning service an integral part of casework counseling.

It soon became natural and easy for the caseworkers to ask, as their talks with clients moved into discussions of their aspirations, if they had any interest in family planning. "How many children do you want?" was often asked. When women expressed interest, referrals to the clinic were made and the good teamwork between the health and welfare agencies assured an effective follow-through.

The most tangible evidence of the value of this program is its effect upon the caseload of the Aid to Families with Dependent Children program. Nationwide, these caseloads have been rising steadily for a number of years, but in Mecklenburg County, the caseload has been going down. In 1961, about 4000 children were in families that depended on public assistance. Since then, there has been a small but consistent decline until today only about 3500 children are in AFDC families.

These programs are indicators of things to come. Obviously, we have a long way to go. Effective family-planning services require personnel appropriately trained in maternal health. Here and in many other aspects of our total challenge in health, the need for skilled professionals is acute.

Specific grants for training programs related to family planning are now being supported by both the Welfare Administration and the Public Health Service. The Children's Bureau, for example, helps to finance training at a number of universities: A grant of more than $150,000 was made to the New York Medical College for training nurses in clinical specialization on maternal and newborn nursing techniques. Another grant was made to Marquette University for $80,000 for continuing education of general practitioners in obstetrics-gynecology care. Adelphi University's School of Social Work received $32,000 for a training institute, primarily for social workers, on high-risk mothers.

In addition, Children's Bureau grants support the teaching of maternal and child health in nine graduate schools of public health and five schools of nursing which include curricula on family-planning and population dynamics. In the long run, the department's activities in the field of research in human reproduction are among the most important being carried on today.

The National Institute of Child Health and Human Development, established in 1963, is now developing basic knowledge on which fertility regulation and family-planning programs, both here and abroad, can be based. Its studies, conducted through research grants for more than 700 projects, are concerned with the clinical, biological, and behavioral aspects of reproduction, including both the short- and long-term effects of different contraceptive practices on the health of the mother and her subsequent child.

As part of its over-all approach to family planning, the institute is also interested in helping couples who are desirous of having children but are not able to do so. In 1966, the institute spent a total of $22.8 million in research on human reproduction. Of this amount, $5 million was devoted to population studies. Estimates for fiscal 1967 are $23.8 million for studies on reproduction and $7 million for population research.

Other research programs conducted through grants by the Children's Bureau are concerned with birth-control studies in relation to the attitudes of different cultural, socioeconomic, ethnic, and religious groups. The information derived from these studies can be useful not only in this country but also in other countries of the world. In addition to research carried out at American universities, the Children's Bureau also assists the Agency for International Development in co-operative research programs of foreign countries.

The relationship between family planning and mental health is another area of growing concern to scientists both in and outside government. A pioneering conference on this subject which was held last January under the joint sponsorship of the National Institutes of Mental Health and the Population Crisis Committee has helped to stimulate increased consideration of the kinds of research that are needed in this largely unexplored area.

The office of education has developed a broad new policy related to sex education and family-life education which will make possible federal support for programs in schools throughout the country. The programs, with those in health and welfare, will be locally developed but they can now receive additional support. There have been a few programs already initiated and there is great interest in this important field.

The Food and Drug Administration also plays an important role in family-planning programs because of its responsibilities relating to safety and effectiveness of new drugs. The recent report of the Advisory Committee on Obstetrics and Gynecology supported the FDA's position on safety and effectiveness of the oral contraceptives and called for an intensified study of possible long-term hazards.

Now let me sum up the federal viewpoint in family-planning, as I see it:

We are committed to a research program that is stronger in emphasis and broader in scope than anything we have done before to accelerate the development of knowledge long overdue on human reproduction, family-planning, and related areas.

We are committed to support programs to train the professional and allied health personnel needed in this expanding effort.

We are committed to support programs in our schools for modern sex education and family-life education. We are committed to assuring the safety and effectiveness of contraceptive drugs presently in use as well as those that will be introduced.

And we are committed to provide support for the development of the services and resources that will make family-planning information and services available to all who seek it, in order that all American families will have the opportunity to exercise wisely their freedom of choice in determining the number and spacing of their children. These objectives are in keeping with everything we do to preserve and advance the quality of human living.

Part IV
APPEALS FOR
REAPPRAISAL

15

FOUR CARDINALS SPEAK

At the fourth session of Vatican Council there were four talks which provided fresh insights on marriage and birth regulation. They all mirror the rich personal values of marriage as well as the need for an effective method of regulating offspring. The talks were given in the discussion of the topic The Church in the Modern World, *and specifically on article 21 dealing with marriage and the family. Delivered on October 29, 1964, in St. Peter's Basilica, the four addresses drew great applause from the Council Fathers and stirred world-wide interest. Because the talks break new ground and reflect the world-wide consensus concerning the need of some effective method of family planning, they are presented here.*

CONJUGAL LOVE IS HOLY
PAUL-EMILE CARDINAL LÉGER OF MONTREAL

Problems concerning the holiness of marriage are, in our times, at the forefront of the preoccupations of the Church. In a great number of countries and among men of all social conditions, there are doubts and anxieties about marriage. Many of the faithful—and often among them some of the best—encounter daily difficulties, search for solutions in accord with their faith, but do not find comfort in the answers given them.

Pastors, particularly confessors, are assailed by doubts and uncertainties and, many times, no longer know what they can or should reply to the faithful. Many theologians feel more and more strongly the need to examine more deeply in a new way the fundamental principles concerning marriage.

All these difficulties reveal the existence of a grave problem and call for the Church to examine with great pastoral concern the doctrine on marriage.

The question of marriage has three aspects: theological, casuistic, and pastoral. I will concern myself here with the theological aspect. It is, moreover, this aspect that holds first place in all renewal in this area.

There are some who fear all renewal in the theology of marriage as if it necessarily proceeds from a forbidden opportunism that would have us search for accommodating solutions that would satisfy a popular wish. In fact, renewal of the theology of marriage, if it has indeed been stimulated by the anxieties of Christian people, proceeds, among the theologians, from a more complete analysis of the problems and, moreover, from some fairly recent discoveries in biology, psychology, and sociology. The final end of this renewal is no other than to enhance the holiness of marriage by a deeper insight into the plan of God.

Many theologians think that the difficulties being encountered today in presentation of the doctrine of marriage arise from an inadequate presentation of the ends of this institution. A certain pessimistic and negative attitude regarding human love, attributable neither to Scripture nor tradition but to philosophies of past centuries, has prevailed, and this has veiled the importance and legitimacy of conjugal love in marriage.

The authors of the present schema wished to renew the doctrine of the ends of marriage. They have taken care to emphasize the love and mutual help of the spouses. It is satisfactory to note also that they avoided the difficulty of putting into opposition the primary and secondary ends of marriage. However, although it keeps to the right track, this schema does not answer the real difficulties and goes only part of the way. It fails to present conjugal love and mutual help as an end of marriage and does not in any way touch on the problem of the purpose of expressions of love in marriage. For this reason, I would like to make some observations about the way of speaking of the ends of marriage.

1. The schema treats well enough of fecundity as a purpose of marriage. It reminds us opportunely that procreation should be governed by prudence and generosity. It would be good, however, to consider this duty of procreation as linked not so much with each act as with the whole state of marriage. I would also like to see the special dignity of parenthood expressed more fully. Parenthood is indeed a participation in the highest level of creation: It contains something of the infinite, since it brings into being a person destined to see the Infinite Himself.

2. It should clearly present human conjugal love—I stress human love which involves both the soul and the body—as a true end of marriage, as something good in itself, with its own characteristics and its own laws. The schema is too hesitant on this point. There is no use in the schema's avoiding the term "secondary end" if it does not present love as being at the service of procreation.

In so important a matter one must state clear principles. Otherwise the fears about conjugal love which have for so long paralyzed our theology would remain. Conjugal love is good and holy in itself and it should be accepted by Christians, without false fears, with its own characteristics and laws. Do not the spouses solemnly promise at their marriage to give themselves this mutual help and love? And unless love is affirmed as an end of marriage, the bond which joins the spouses will not be correctly understood. In marriage the spouses consider each other not as mere procreators but as persons loved for their own sakes.

3. However, it is not sufficient to establish clearly the doctrine which concerns marriage as a state. Unless the problem of the purpose of the actions themselves is dealt with in its most general principles, the difficulties which preoccupy spouses and pastors cannot be solved and a profound and adequate renewal of the philosophy of marriage will not be attained.

It must also be stated that the intimate union of the spouses also finds a purpose in love. And this end is truly "the end of the act itself" (*finis operis*), lawful in itself, even when it is not ordained to procreation. Moreover, by such a statement the Council would be only ratifying in the order of principles a practice which the Church has approved, as we know; for many centuries. For centuries, indeed, union of the spouses has been considered lawful even when procreation was known to be impossible.

Even if it implies nothing new, the declaration of principles which I put forward will not be without its importance in the better determination of the morality of different cases.

To conclude: Could this Council, without fear or reticence, clearly proclaim the two ends of marriage as equally good and holy? Once that is done, the moral theologians, doctors, psychologists, and other experts can much more easily determine for particular cases the duties both of procreation and of love.

An Honest Doubt Arises
Bernard Cardinal Alfrink of Utrecht, the Netherlands

To all priests engaged in pastoral work, the anxieties and very great difficulties of married life are brought by many of the faithful of good will who wish to fulfill the duties of their state generously. These difficulties often lead to estrangement from the Church. However, the spiritual struggle can be so tiring that it can no longer be endured without harming human values, including the highest value of marriage itself, namely fidelity.

It is clear that the Church, as the guardian of divine law, can never, because of human difficulties, however great, change that law by adapting it to human incapacity. Moreover, it is evident that sociological analysis of these difficulties cannot solve the moral question of human acts.

The Church cannot indulge in what is called "situation ethics," according to which the absolute moral norm is said to lose its force in certain circumstances. The Church, too, always professes that sacrifice and self-denial belong to the essence of Christian life. But not only the cross but also the joy of the Resurrection pertains to the Christian life, and God does not take pleasure in the difficulties of man.

Indeed, the difficulties of married life are often of such a kind that in fact a serious problem arises between two values of marriage, namely, on the one hand the value of procreation, and on the other the value of human and Christian education of the children.

This conflict can be avoided only when there is conjugal love between the parents, being sustained and increased by sexual intercourse. This conflict is not between two distinct values. For, without the love and fidelity of the spouses, strengthened by the fostering of love (as the schema rightly calls it) the very motive of procreation is morally endangered.

The real question is this: Given the moral conflict in performing one and the same act, if in this act the spouses wish to preserve the biological end, their human duty of educating their future and even their existing children in a proper Christian way is harmed. If, however, they wish to preserve the fidelity of the marriage and the duty of educating their children, the question is whether, besides periodic continence (which many married people practice with great Christian virtue but which more often is attempted with great difficulty) or complete continence (which demands, among other things, of spouses a greater moral strength than they are normally supposed to have), only one solution is available—namely, performing the act and excluding offspring, at least in this particular set.

It is evident that if this prevention of offspring is brought about by the use of means which are undoubtedly intrinsically bad, the Church can never admit the sacrifice of a particular value in marriage in order to preserve the total value of marriage.

But with the new anthropological knowledge, especially the growing recognition of the essential distinction between a mere biological sexuality and human sexuality, an honest doubt is arising among many married people and also among scientists and some theologians regarding at least the arguments used to prove that the only efficacious moral and Christian solution to such conflicts in the married life of the faithful of good will is complete or periodic continence.

The situation or the state of the problem is too serious to permit the Church to decide this real conflict hastily and perhaps prematurely. The Church must be careful to preserve the purity of divine law, but she must also be solicitous about human problems.

The Church must investigate in a holy and diligent way, so that all Christians may know that, whatever the answer should be, it will be stated with great charity and by all the means which the various sciences can supply. Therefore, it is right to rejoice at the establishment of a commission of selected experts who are dealing with this question.

Only if there is real certainty regarding the knowledge of the true content of divine law can and must the Church bind or free the consciences of her faithful. Finally, because of the very rapid progress of science, particularly medicine and the other sciences which concern human life by which scientific progress brings new ethical and moral problems to light day by day, the question can be asked whether the Church does not need nowadays a permanent commission of experts in philosophy and theology and also in the field of science. Because of her pastoral solicitude this commission should follow up the evolution of these sciences immediately, lest the Church would come to consider and attempt to solve these problems too late.

A BACHELOR PSYCHOSIS?
MELCHITE PATRIARCH MAXIMOS IV SAIGH OF ANTIOCH

Today I want to draw the attention of this venerable assembly to a special moral point: birth regulation. The main virtue we need in undertaking this discussion, in a council which wishes to be pastoral, is the courage to tackle the problems of the hour directly in the love of Christ and of souls. Because among the agonizing and burdensome problems which beset masses of humanity today is that of birth control. It is an urgent problem because it lies at the root of a great crisis of the Catholic conscience.

There is a question here of a break between the official doctrine of the Church and the contrary practice of the immense majority of Christian couples. The authority of the Church has been called into question on a vast scale. The faithful find themselves forced to live in conflict with the law of the Church, far from the sacraments, in constant anguish, unable to find a viable solution between two contradictory imperatives: conscience and normal married life.

On the other hand, on the social plane, demographic pressures in certain countries of particularly heavy population prevent any increase in the standard of living and condemn hundreds of millions of human beings to unworthy and hopeless misery. The Council must find a practical solution. This is a pastoral duty. It must say if God really wishes this enfeebling and unnatural impasse.

Venerable Fathers, be aware in the Lord, who died and rose again for the salvation of men, of the really sad crises of conscience of our faithful, and have the courage to tackle this question without prejudice.

Frankly, can the official positions of the Church in this matter not be reviewed in the light of modern theological, medical, psychological, and sociological science? In marriage, the development of personality and its integration into the creative plan of God are all one. Thus, the end of marriage should not be divided into "primary" and "secondary." This consideration opens new perspectives concerning the morality of conjugal behavior considered as a whole.

And are we not entitled to ask if certain positions are not the outcome of outmoded ideas and, perhaps, a bachelor psychosis on the part of those unacquainted with this sector of life? Are we not, perhaps unwillingly, setting up a Manichaean conception of man and the world, in which the work of the flesh, vitiated in itself, is tolerated only in view of children? Is the external biological rectitude of an act the only criterion of morality, independent of family life, of its moral, conjugal, and family climate, and of the grave imperatives of prudence which must be the basic rule of all our human activity?

Secondly, does modern exegesis not require of us greater care in the interpretation of the two passages from Genesis—"increase and multiply," and that concerning Onan, so long used as the classic scriptural support for the radical condemnation of contraception?

How the Christian conscience felt relieved when Pope Paul announced to the world that the problem of birth control and family morality "is under study, a study as extensive and deep as possible, that is, as serious and honest as the great importance of this problem requires. The Church must proclaim this law of God in the light of the scientific, social, and psychological truths which, in recent times, have been the object of study and scholarship."

Further, given the extent and gravity of this problem which concerns the whole world, we ask that this study should be conducted by theologians, doctors, psychologists, and sociologists, to find its normal solution. The collaboration of outstanding married Christians is also necessary. In addition, is it not following the ecumenical line of the Council to open a dialogue on this subject with other Christian churches and even with the thinkers of other religions?

Are we not here face to face with a problem common to all humanity? Shouldn't the Church open itself to the non-Christian as well as the Christian world? Is it not the leaven that is to make the dough rise? So it must come, in this area as in all other matters of interest to humanity, to positive results giving peace to the conscience.

Far from me to minimize the delicacy of and the gravity of the subject, or of eventual abuses; but here as elsewhere, isn't it the duty of the Church to educate the moral sense of her children, to form them in moral responsibility, personal and communitarian, profoundly rooted in Christ, rather than to envelop it in a net of prescriptions and commandments, and to demand that they purely and simply conform to these with their eyes closed? For ourselves, let us open our eyes and be practical. Let us see things as they are and not as we would like them to be. Otherwise we risk speaking in a desert. What is at stake is the future of the mission of the Church in the world.

Let us loyally and effectively put into practice the declaration of Pope Paul opening the second session of the Council: "Let the world know this: The Church looks upon the world with profound understanding, with a sincere admiration, with a sincere intention not to subjugate but to serve it, not to despise it but to appreciate it, not to condemn it but to support and save it."

One Galileo Case Is Enough
Leo Joseph Cardinal Suenens of Malines-Brussels, Belgium

Regarding No. 21, dealing with the dignity of marriage and on the family, I would like to make some observations. We all know how crucial the question of marriage, and in particular of birth control, is for the world and for the Church. Consequently:

1. It seems to me indispensable to add to the text some elements of doctrine that are found in the annexes. That means a reworking of the text to present a doctrinal synthesis that would be more profound, more coherent and biblical. I am giving the commission, in writing, an attempt at such synthesis.

2. It seems to me also indispensable that the Council commission work in close harmony with the commission which the Holy Father has very happily organized for a broad and deep study of these problems.

3. May I be permitted to express the wish that this commission undertake a very far-reaching inquiry among moralists of renown coming from the entire world, among scholars and university faculties of

various disciplines among the laity, both men and women, and among Christian couples.

It would be desirable that the names of the members of this commission be made known in such a way that they might receive the broadest possible information and be truly representative of the people of God.

4. So that this commission may know the spirit in which the Council sees these problems, it seems to me essential to formulate some basic orientations for the success of its work.

A. In the Area of Faith

The first work of this commission is in the area of faith, and should consist in this: to study whether up to now we have given sufficient emphasis to all aspects of the teaching of the Church on marriage.

To be sure, it is not a question of modifying or of casting doubt on the truly traditional teaching of the Church. That would be folly! It is a question of knowing whether we have opened our hearts completely to the Holy Spirit in order to understand the divine truth.

The Bible is always the same. But no generation can take pride in having fully perceived the unfathomable riches of Christ. The Holy Spirit has been promised to us to introduce us progressively to the fullness of the truth.

Thus the Church has never to repudiate a truth that it once taught, but according as, and in the measure that, she progresses in a deeper study of the Gospel, she can and she must integrate this truth in a richer synthesis and bring out the fuller fruitfulness of the same principles. In this way the Church draws from her treasure things new and things old.

This established, it is important to examine if we have maintained in perfect balance all aspects of the teaching of the Church on marriage. It may be that we have accentuated the Gospel text "increase and multiply" to such a point that we have obscured another text, "and they will be two in one flesh." These two truths are central and both are scriptural; they must illuminate each other in the light of the full truth that is revealed to us in our Lord Jesus Christ.

St. Paul, in effect, has given to Christian marriage, as a prototype, the very love of Christ for His Church. This "two in one" is a mystery of interpersonal communion, gratified and sanctified by the sacrament of marriage. And this union is of such profundity that divorce can never separate two whom God unites as one.

Also, it is for the commission to tell us whether we have excessively stressed the first end, procreation, at the expense of another equally important end, that is, growth in conjugal unity.

In the same way, it is up to this commission to deal with the immense problem arising from the population explosion and overpopulation in many areas of the world. For the first time we must proceed with such a study in the light of the faith. It is difficult, but the world, whether consciously or not, waits for the Church to express her thought and to be a "light for the nations."

Let no one say that in this way we open the way to moral laxity. The problem confronts us not because the faithful try to satisfy their passions and their egotism but because thousands of them try with anguish to live in double fidelity to the doctrine of the Church and to the demands of conjugal and parental love.

B. In the Area of Natural Ethics and Science

The second task of the commission lies in the area of scientific progress and deeper knowledge of natural ethics. The commission should examine whether classical doctrine, especially that of the manuals, takes sufficient account of the new knowledge of modern science. We have made progress since Aristotle (and even since St. Augustine), and we have discovered the complexity with which the real or the biological interferes with the psychological, the conscious with the subconscious.

New possibilities are constantly discovered in man of his power to direct the course of nature. From this, then, emerges a greater understanding of the unity of man, both in his being as incarnated spirit and in the dynamics of his whole life—a unity which is like the heart of Thomistic anthropology. There follows, equally, a more exact estimate of his rational power over the world confided to him. Who does not see that we will perhaps be led in this way to further studies on the question of what is "according to or against nature"? We will follow the progress of science.

I beg you, my brother bishops, let us avoid a new "Galileo case." One is enough for the Church. It will be for the commission to integrate new elements into the total understanding and to submit its conclusions to the supreme magisterium. Let it not be said that by this new synthesis we give in to situation ethics. The exposition of doctrine, unchangeable in its principles, must take into account contingent factors and changes in the course of history. That is what the popes did who, in turn, wrote *Rerum Novarum, Quadrigesimo Anno,* and *Mater et Magistra* to express the same principles more precisely in terms of new times.

Venerable brothers, we do not have the right to be quiet. Let us not fear to begin the study of these problems. It is for the welfare of souls, of our families, and of the world. Let us listen to the Holy Spirit, accepting at the same time and totally every particle of truth that He suggests to us, recalling the words of the Lord, "The truth—both natural and supernatural—total and living—will set you free."

What was the significance of the cardinal's statement that one Galileo case is "enough for the Church"? Here in a nutshell is the Galileo affair. On the evening of January 11, 1610, Galileo perceived through a rude telescope of his own devising that Venus displayed phases like the moon. He thus confirmed with observable data the conclusion of Copernicus that the earth is not the fixed, immovable center of the universe but revolves about the sun.

This shook the centuries-old belief of mankind to its very foundations and prompted theologians, scriptural scholars, and churchmen to call him a "heretic," "infidel," and "atheist." Some asserted that his "pretended discovery vitiates the whole Christian plan of salvation." Others declared that "it upsets the whole basis of theology."

Theologians clamored for his condemnation because his teaching was "contrary to Scripture." At the order of Pope Paul V, Cardinal Bellarmine commanded Galileo to renounce his teaching "that the earth moves" and not "to hold, teach, or defend it in any way whatsoever, verbally or in writing."

In March 1616, the Congregation of the Index condemned his teaching as "directly contrary to Holy Scripture." Its condemnation was fully approved by the Pope. Galileo continued his work and writings and published the Dialogue *and his greatest work,* Discourses Concerning Two New Sciences.

He was again summoned before the Inquisition, condemned for heresy, and forced to sign the humiliating retraction: "I, Galileo, in my seventieth year, being a prisoner and on my knees, and before Your Eminence, having before my eyes the Holy Gospel, which I touch with my hands, abjure, curse, and detest the error and the heresy that the sun is the center of the universe and immovable and that the earth is not its center and that it moves."

In discussing the condemnation of Galileo, Father John Gerald, S.J., writes: "In thus acting, it is undeniable that the ecclesiastical authorities committed a grave and deplorable error, and sanctioned an altogether false principle as to the proper use of Scripture."

This was surely bad enough. But they made matters worse by keeping on the Index of Prohibited Books Galileo's works and all others teaching the same truths for more than two centuries! This is why Cardinal Suenens said: "I beg you, my brother bishops, let us avoid a new 'Galileo case.'" In short, throughout history the Church has opposed every new finding of science that might shock or upset the traditional belief of any of its members, no matter how naïve, uneducated, and illiterate they might be. It finally accepted the new finding only after virtually the whole civilized world had done so.

16

CATHOLIC SCHOLARS
APPEAL TO THE POPE

The growing conviction of Catholic scholars throughout the world that the Church must sanction some simple and effective means of regulating births, if mankind is not to be faced with famine, disaster, and chaos, was expressed in an appeal to Pope Paul VI and Vatican Council II. In October 1964, an international group of Catholic laymen of twelve learned professions petitioned the highest ecclesiastical authorities to make a "far-reaching appraisal" of the Church's teachings on birth regulation.

The 182 signatories of the petition, from twelve countries in Europe and the Americas, respectfully left the determination of the issues to Church officials. They pointed out, however, that the present ban on any chemical or mechanical means for contraception was based on a view of "natural law" that failed to take sufficient cognizance of modern developments in physical and psychological sciences.

It was man's interference with the so-called "natural law" in eliminating deadly plagues and in upsetting the biological balance, the statement noted, that had produced the overpopulation problems that made the regulation of births an urgent and inescapable necessity. The scholars pointed out that the implied refusal of the Church to come to grips with the problem realistically had made Catholic doctors and scientists "painfully aware" of a conflict between their professional and religious convictions in dealing with patients who consulted them.

Furthermore, the petitioners declared, priests have also been compelled to make a most unfortunate distinction between a formal directive—the absolute ban on artificial contraceptive means—and its application in practice. "Man's intervention in nature can raise delicate problems," the scholars observed, "but he has a norm for their solution in the over-all good of the individual and mankind. It is not a question of denying the absolute sovereignty of God, but of recognizing man's part in the creative process for which God has endowed him with intelligence and will."

In short, through the discoveries of medical science God has shared His providence with man and has thus enabled married couples to regulate the number of offspring in accordance with their health, resources, and the population needs of the region in which they live. It was this basic responsibility of man today that was the central theme of the document distributed to the more than 2000 bishops and cardinals attending Vatican Council on the eve of the discussion of the important draft on *The Church in the Modern World.* This draft contains sections indicating that the Church is considering the problem of family planning, but has not yet arrived at any affirmative conclusions.

Among the signers of the document are physicians, psychologists, psychiatrists, philosophers, jurists, editors, authors, publishers, sociologists, gynecologists, legislators, lawyers, and educators. They come from Britain, Belgium, Bolivia, Australia, Austria, France, the Congo, Italy, The Netherlands, Canada, West Germany, and the United States.

A random sampling of the signatories included J. B. Bouckairt, professor of physiology at Louvain University, Belgium; Richard J. Blackwell, associate professor of philosophy at St. Louis University; Roberto Melchoir, an officer of a Catholic social organization of La Paz, Bolivia; Joseph Sullivan, associate professor of psychiatry at Cornell University; Joseph T. English, chief psychologist of the U. S. Peace Corps; and Philip J. Scharper, editor-president of the Religious Education of the United States and Canada.

In the draft on *The Church in the Modern World,* the Council recognizes the conflict between the "intimate drive of conjugal love" and the "sense of responsibility" of parents for refraining from producing more children than they can care for adequately. The document urges scientists, married laymen, and theologians to collaborate on a profound investigation and study of the problem. It requests Catholic married couples "not to be discouraged" if the Church is unable immediately to resolve the problems of human sexuality.

Profoundly influencing the traditional thought of the Church have been the writings of St. Augustine in the fifth century. He maintained that one of the sources of man's inherent sinfulness was the "concupiscence" which accompanied the act of procreation, thus being largely responsible for the Church's traditional conception of the intrinsic evil of human sexuality.

Challenging this view, the scholarly signatories of the appeal assert on the basis of modern psychological findings: "Ordered human sexuality, within the framework of married life, undoubtedly contributes to the development of the whole person." The whole document, well reasoned and reflecting the findings of all the relevant sciences, merits careful reading and study.

APPEAL TO POPE PAUL VI AND ECUMENICAL COUNCIL BY 182 CATHOLIC SCHOLARS OF EUROPE, BRITAIN, NORTH AND SOUTH AMERICA

The signers of the present document are laymen, engaged in diverse kinds of temporal activity, who believe that dialogue within the Church, most recently solicited by the encyclical of the Sovereign Pontiff, can be of great utility since we are all faced with the task of creating a fruitful exchange between the world and the teaching of Christ. The presence of the Church in the world demands that she concern herself with the problems which face us at this moment regarding the family in general and regulation of human fertility in particular.

It would be difficult to overestimate the human dimension of the problems involved. On the one hand, it is well known that millions of couples who are Christians in good faith are finding immense difficulty in reconciling the diverse aims of marriage—procreation, education, and conjugal love—within the bounds of existing directives. All this has resulted in countless conflicts: distortions of conscience, exit from the

Church, and breakdown of family unity. We have also seen develop a pastoral approach obliged to introduce unfortunate distinctions between the formal directives and their application.

On the other hand, an increasing number of professional persons—in the field of medicine or demography, for example—feel themselves torn apart by the conflict between their concern for the well-being of man and certain aspects of Catholic teaching. We believe that grave difficulties regarding teaching underlie these problems aggravating the life of Christians. That teaching must be submitted to a yet deeper examination and confronted with the insights of the contemporary scene.

A large part of the world's population is confronted with demographical problems—and this in increasing measure. The fertility potential of the human species on the biological level is very high—something necessary at one time to compensate for the high mortality rate indigenous to primitive man. To the extent that this mortality rate has been progressively lowered through human ingenuity, the species is faced with a superabundant fertility. Whatever might be said about a lack of sufficient population or births in certain regions, man as a whole cannot avoid the question of the regulation of fertility. Neither can the individual family.

If man by his nature has the right to intervene in the physical process, it is no less true that he must respect the appropriate means and manner of acting. This means, of course, paying particular attention to the human values engaged here: physical well-being, psychic health, and the harmony of family and of the couple. But at the same time, these cannot lack efficacy.

The frame of mind with which we have approached these problems and the practical applications they entail have generally stemmed from a set of conceptions about the natural law. It seems to us that one ought to exercise extreme prudence in his formulation of this law and the meanings he may attribute to it.

The natural law in its formulation is the fruit of reflection upon the human condition and the demands associated with it. It would be strange to conceive it in a manner other than oriented toward the realization of human nature in its totality and animated by respect for human life and the human person. Man's intervention in nature can pose problems which are delicate, but which nonetheless find their norms in the good of man and humanity. There is no question of denying the absolute sovereignty of God but simply of recognizing the responsibility which God has left to human reason.

If this be the case, it seems out of the question that a conflict might exist between a natural law based on respect for human values and a control of fertility—or any means employed to this end—which has in mind the complete human good. Similarly, it seems out of the question that a natural law which tends to the total human good could find itself in oppposition to man's mastery over physical processes—including procreation—exercised with an aim to the same human good. We have long been used to being taught that man could exercise his control over this domain in a morally legitimate manner—as in surgery, organ transplantation, and even the sacrifice of one's life freely or under orders, when a higher good be at stake.

In fact, demographical problems have arisen as a direct consequence of man's active intervention in the biological order—eliminating factors inimical to life. In the face of this, it becomes increasingly difficult to understand how a relative aspect of the biological order can be considered as the supreme norm governing any form of compensating intervention in this area.

Another point of view on the question is offered by our psychological understanding, which has contributed in large measure to clarifying the meaning of sexuality. On the one hand, we have become aware of the continuous and exuberant character of spermatogenesis—a permanent process of creation and reabsorption of millions of spermatozoids. On the other hand, we are conscious of the temporal limitations on fecundity in the woman. And further, the sexual behavior of woman is not subject to the tyrannical influence of periodic hormonal secretions, as is the case with inferior mammals.

It happens, then, that the link between the sex act and procreation is much less strict even on the physiological plane than it has long been thought to be. Given the fact that the majority of sex acts are now known to be infertile, it is no longer possible to consider fertility as the direct end or immediate meaning of each particular act. What is known and felt to be impossible cannot be considered as an end.

In this perspective, the question of fertility broadens to include a number of acts, all of which pertain to conjugal life. Certain difficulties attach to the fact that these facts have only been partially assimilated into the teaching of the Church.

According to that teaching, one may intend that an act be infertile, but the method employed to assure this infertility is judged licit only to the extent that it does not deprive the act of its procreative power. Thus a latent conflict appears in every admitted use of fertility regulation: The sex act will be effectively and intentionally infertile on the one hand, but conserves in its exterior form what is thought to represent its "fertile character." Hence it is alleged that within the present framework, one cannot countenance the regulation of fertility except at the price of a contradiction between the intentional and effective content of an act and its exterior form.

Psychological insight together with the progressive personalizing of human relations in many sectors of life has contributed to a re-evaluation of the positive role of affective and physical elements in the realization of conjugal unity. There is no doubt that human sexuality, as a part of the life of the couple, contributes to the development of the human person. Its eminent dignity merits the continual solicitude of the Church.

Even accepting procreation as the primary objective of the institution of marriage, plenty of room remains to recognize the profound unity as well as the dynamic character of the aims of marriage. The total end of marriage is the family: The complete and lasting unity of two persons in conjugal love constitutes the base of a fertility really human. This unity, by which the individual transcends himself in orienting his life around the other, is also the ideal climate in which a young life can develop and blossom in a balanced way.

This progression toward unity must find an outlet for realization during the entire span of life. The sexual bond between the spouses is integrated into their total humanity and so merits the place of an essential element in their unity. The human values in question lead us to recognize limits to conjugal continence—as did the apostle Paul. It must be the responsibility of the spouses to determine them, even when faced with the question of regulation of fertility.

Human knowledge has helped shed light on the multiple dimensions of the sexual bond between humans, without denying any values hitherto acknowledged. Thus science has underlined interpersonal values—values the Church had already recognized as part of conjugal intimacy. Similarly with a conception of sexuality, which remains intimately linked to fertility even if it be quite distinct from it. For the Christian, the intention to devote himself to his family in full awareness of the range of his human responsibilities will always be in opposition to a mentality inimical to fertility.

We believe that it is our duty to call your attention to the conclusions which follow from these considerations. It was not our intention to sketch out a doctrinal synthesis. We have merely indicated the data which must be integrated into the teaching and the practice of Catholic marriage as part of the acquisitions of our time. These insights show that certain conceptions, especially those stemming from a particular vision of the natural order and man's rights over his body, as well as the meaning given to the sex act, are at least open for discussion.

We would request that the teaching Church give less weight to certain formulations which have been largely determined by their historical context. We ask besides that a way might be opened which permits the theology and the living thought of the Church to integrate contemporary scientific and philosophical findings. We are convinced that one must make room for a conception of the natural order which does not exclude an *efficacious* responsibility of man toward procreation. By the same token, it seems indispensable not to exclude a conception of the morality of the sex act as it is lived in the context of conjugal love—and depending not so much on the direct fertility of each *particular* act as on the generosity of an *entire* conjugal life to fertility.

We are convinced that we are responding to the desires of many, many Christians in asking that a conception of marriage be developed in which *interpersonal* relations are given their full due.

Due to the complexity of the questions raised and their effect on the lives of millions of human beings, we can only hope the final process of integration will represent the fruit of a period of maturation. This will be required not only for sufficient reflection but also for the formation of consciences, which will be called to an even greater personal responsibility.

We present these considerations with sentiments of profound respect, convinced that searching for the truth for the spiritual good of man is the first duty of every person. We believe that the Church could assist the world in working out a moral synthesis in which the binding human *responsibility* to regulate fecundity will be integrated into a personalist vision of marriage and an authentic conjugal spirituality.

MORE CATHOLIC SCHOLARS APPEAL

Two years later, in June 1966, some 600 Catholic intellectuals from Europe, Britain, and the Americas presented a new appeal for the liberalization of the Church's teaching on birth control, consistent with modern concepts of the nature of man and natural law. The appeal was addressed to the "Magisterium of the Church," a term which includes both Pope Paul VI and the mixed commission of prelates, priests, and laymen that was then meeting in Rome in an effort to draft a recommendation on the issue for the Pope.

The document points out that the Church's present ruling that partial or total abstinence from sexual relations is the only lawful means for limitation of fecundity is *no longer* justified either theologically or scientifically. "Furthermore," the large international group of noted Catholic scholars declares, "it is becoming more and more obvious that in these matters it is impossible to lay down or maintain moral directives which are too particularized on the technical or physical levels without provoking a major crisis of conscience and endangering the permanency and eminent dignity of the Christian message."

The petition presents as urgent reasons for revising the birth-control ruling the new formulations of conjugal love accepted by the Vatican Council, the dangers of an unchecked "population explosion," basic human values, and a concept of natural law that does not accept mere *biological* function as an *absolute*.

The appeal calls attention to the well-known "fact that a very large number of Catholic couples decide in conscience and for objective reasons that mere physiological integrity does not constitute an essential

prerequisite governing the truly human character of each conjugal act."
In other words, they are using mechanical or chemical means of practicing birth control in accordance with their conscientious convictions.

Alluding to the rulings against such usage by Popes Pius X and
Pius XII, the signers declare: "These directives, however, belong to their
particular historical contexts and should be understood as having been
inspired by a then contemporaneous interpretation of the natural law
which is now recognized as deficient." They then point out that "the
notion of respect due to biological integrity [that is, the inviolability
of biological processes] is not so absolute as not to be subordinated to
the principle of the good of the human person, seen in all its aspects."
The document stresses the dangers of unchecked human fecundity to
the human race and to the maximum development of the individual.
It then warns: "The Church cannot take the responsibility before history of minimizing one of the main problems which humanity must
face, let alone of constituting an obstacle to general research into real
solutions: Humanity expects a moral contribution from one of the
great spiritual forces of the world."
The signers of the appeal include doctors, jurists, writers, editors,
university professors, engineers, administrators, and scientists conducting research in all the disciplines bearing upon birth regulation and
the population problem. They are citizens of most of the Western
European countries, the United States, Canada, and seven Latin-American countries. Many of those who signed the previous appeal of the
182 scholars are included in the present list.
Among the seventy-three signatories from the United States are Dr.
John Rock of Brookline, Massachusetts, a pioneer in the development
of the progestational pill regulating conception; Daniel Callahan, associate editor of *Commonweal* magazine; Michael Novak of Stanford
University; Dr. William T. Liu of the sociology department of Notre
Dame, and twenty other members of the Notre Dame faculty.
Probably never before did so many noted Catholic scholars from so
many disciplines and from so many countries unite to present to the
highest authorities of the Church an appeal of such world-wide significance, urgence, and importance. It is known that the message reached
Pope Paul and was shared by him with the members of the papal

commission dealing with this problem. Drawn up with great care, the appeal merits careful reading and study.

In addressing themselves once again to the hierarchy of the Church, the signatories of this document, deeply grateful for the sympathetic reception given to the previous address to the Council, would like to offer a contribution to the dialogue between the world of today and the truth of Christ.

Vatican Council II has recently formulated a doctrine of marriage that has shown itself capable of integrating the eternal values of Christianity with various contemporary insights, such as a consciousness of the dignity of the whole man in his unity of body and soul, and an understanding of marriage as a community of persons called to a responsible fecundity.

The successful assimilation of these elements shows, too, that the Church has developed a more detached attitude to certain past formulations which do not belong to the essential heritage of Christianity. We are thinking of, among others, the dualist concept of man, which led to a sort of pessimism in its approach to the body; of a rather cosmological view of the natural law, giving biological structures a directly determining role in human actions; of an excessively sociojuridical view of marriage, which fails to do justice to all the requirements of the personal element.

The historically important doctrinal development cannot fail to bring its repercussions in the pastoral field. However, some influences are making themselves felt which threaten to undermine all prudent progress. We therefore feel it our duty to express our apprehension and to recall the seriousness of the problems.

Human fecundity today poses very real problems which a large part of the Catholic community has not yet sufficiently appreciated.

For some twenty years many technically underdeveloped countries have been experiencing the phenomenon which has been called the "demographic explosion." Human fecundity is potentially very high since it is destined to guarantee survival in the most unfavorable conditions. It can give rise to an excessive local level of effective reproduction as soon as chances of survival for both infants and adults increase, thanks to human intervention, in the medical field in particular.

Experts in various fields and scientists, however much they may differ on the question of appreciating the possibilities of developments in the production and the distribution of goods, are virtually in agreement in recognizing that if the human race were not to apply some restriction to its power of biological fecundity it would, in a relatively near future, endanger essential human values. Thus many nations are finding themselves faced with the relatively new and often urgent task of regulating fecundity.

But the realization of this task is conditioned in the first place by the existence of appropriate motivations in populations. Moreover the possibilities of applying different techniques are being seen to be a function of the intellectual and psychological dispositions of the individual. Hence methods of control based on continence are particularly unsuitable as a remedy for the great problems of population.

In the technically developed countries the situation appears in a different light. Some regulation of fecundity is generally carried out in these countries under the influence of sociological motivations, many of them a positive help in the development of truly human values. Thus, for example, the lengthening of the time of education, the social advancement of woman, the high material requirements of upholding human dignity in the social context, all these require great efforts from parents if they are to prepare their children decently for life.

Consequently the great majority of married couples are forced, often to their regret, to practice some form of birth control during the greater part of their married life. The fact that in a considerable proportion of cases the methods of periodic continence are so uncertain again render them, already from a merely technical point of view, unsuitable to be considered a sole remedy to the problem of the control of fecundity.

This control of fecundity is compatible with a very positive attitude to life, and the use of contraception is not necessarily inspired by any hedonistic attitude. The gap which has opened up throughout the world between the human race's potential for effective reproduction and its more limited possibilities of fulfillment poses real and even agonizing problems. For a number of nations, as for innumerable well-intentioned married couples, an effective and practical regulation of fecundity is not only a *necessity* but also an immediate *duty*.

The Church cannot take the responsibility before history of minimizing one of the main problems which humanity must face, let alone of constituting an obstacle to general research into real solutions. Humanity expects a positive moral contribution from one of the great spiritual forces of the world.

The basis of any authentically Christian ethic is respect and love for the human person, gifted with the powers of freedom and reason, created in the image of the living God.

This principle, a foundation for the dialogue with the world of to-day, was unequivocally put forward by the Council as the basis of its doctrine on marriage. It implies man's effective responsibility for the preservation and active realization of various human values, those of the corporality included.

The various aspects of the problem of fecundity, such as the moral judgment to be made on the physiological integrality of the different factors of reproduction, must be properly appreciated in the light of this principle. What is the significance of this physiological integrality in the sum total of the values of married life, made up, as it is, of conjugal unity and responsible fecundity? The Council is referring to the personal values and in underlining their transcendent dimensions is not subordinating them to the requirement of permanent conformity to the biological order. In present conditions, in fact, it is no longer possible to consider the total preservation of this biological order as a *sine qua non* condition of human integrity.

It is true that certain directives have in the past been expressed in strict enough terms, but these belong to their historical context and furthermore were inspired by a then current interpretation of natural law now recognized as deficient. The theological concept on which these directives were based—that of a God who is master and owner of the body—requires an extremely delicately nuanced interpretation if it is not to smack of anthropomorphism and to imply a dualist philosophy of man. Furthermore the legitimacy of various important interventions in human biological processes which is gradually being recognized, such as the transplantation of organs for serious reasons, indicates that the notion of respect due to biological integrity is not so absolute that it ought not to be subordinated to the principle of the good of the whole human person.

Certain recent theological tendencies, which try to deduce from a philosophy of man his obligation to submit unconditionally to his biological structures, in general or more particularly in sexual matters, should be treated with caution, to say the least. Reservations must also be made with regard to a theological trend which, failing to distinguish sufficiently the different levels, leads to a new determinism opposed to personalism, by turning valid psychological opinions into absolute moral law.

There are also various objective facts which prevent one from making the biological integrity of human functions an absolute condition of morality.

In the first place, this question must be seen in the total context of a universal human problem. The doctrine of the Council itself is based not on a pre-existing order implying *a priori* norms but on the values of the human person. One cannot here neglect human experience. Convictions in this matter, progressively acquired by various human and Christian communities, must therefore be taken seriously into account.

Then from the medical and scientific points of view, the thesis which would give absolute primacy to physiological integrality is debatable. It leads to the restriction of medical practice within limits which many specialists judge in all conscience to be contrary to the real good of the person.

Finally we should take into account the significance of the fact that a very large number of fervent and generous Catholic married couples, placed in the situation of having to choose an attitude which will best safeguard the multiple objectives of their marriage, including the wholeness, the integrity, of their conjugal life, decide in conscience that physiological integrality does not constitute a prequisite which governs the truly human character of each conjugal act.

It is thus indisputable that today we are faced with an open question which the principle of *possessio juris* cannot invalidate. This is why we feel such anxiety in the face of a tendency to suggest that the problem should be solved on the disciplinary and pastoral level simply by maintaining the old directives, which for several objective reasons are today doubtful. This would entail a grave risk of establishing a fatal divergence between ecclesiastical teaching and the deep insight of the world of today.

Conclusions

This brief analysis of some major aspects of these problems suggests certain conclusions which we would like to express. Techniques alone are not sufficient to resolve either demographic problems or the difficulties of individual couples. Both nations and individuals require moral motivations to guide them in the exercise of their fecundity and to give a meaning to their choices. The need for such motivations is being felt more and more, both where the phenomenon is one of underpopulation and where nations are threatened with overpopulation.

This presents the Church with a specific task. There is, in fact, no other spiritual power which could with more authority invite couples to responsibility in the exercise of their fecundity which should be generous, also by caring for the common good in the concrete sociological conditions of their surroundings.

The Catholic doctrine of marriage as formulated by the Council, based as it is on the respect due to the human person, offers married couples a noble ideal and permits them to show themselves faithful to their vocation in the present time. Not yet sufficiently understood, it still needs to be presented with clarity, free from all equivocation, in particular from any interpretation which would tend to fall back on a physicist conception of the natural law. By making such a message heard, basing it on the great principles which are hers to safeguard, the Church would make her uniquely positive and irreplaceable contribution to solving one of the great problems of the present day.

Certainly such a general pronouncement would not resolve everything. For an adequate reply to be given to the questions which will continue to be asked in the vast field of fecundity and the family, it is of primary importance that there should be normal conditions for study established, that the research which is being undertaken should benefit "from a spirit of confidence and attitude of openness" to quote the wish already expressed in the address to the Council. We ask therefore that a place be found, within the framework of doctrinal unity indicated by the Council, for an acceptance of the diversity of attitudes to these questions which is bound to exist at present and does no more than reflect the varying appreciations of the significance of new scientific and philosophic developments in time of transition.

Furthermore it is becoming more and more obvious that in these matters it is impossible to lay down or maintain too particularized moral directives without provoking a major crisis of conscience and endangering the permanency and eminent dignity of the Christian message.

Finally it seems that an open invitation to common research, far from constituting a danger to religious unity, could in fact safeguard the cohesion of the Catholic world in dialogue and open the way to that future synthesis hoped for by all.

Consequently we hope that the teaching authority will show confidence in the spiritual maturity of the Catholic community. Each member of the People of God has the right and even the duty to contribute to this research to the extent of his ability. The signatories to this address have been guided by the desire to make their modest contribution to this task, and it is with respect that they offer this document to the consideration of the Catholic hierarchy.

17

APPEALS OF SCIENTISTS, THEOLOGIANS, AND SCHOLARS

by John A. O'Brien

With the world's inhabitants increasing each year by about fifty million, the population problem becomes yearly more acute and the need for constructive action to regulate that growth becomes more urgent. Hence it was that two large groups of Nobel prize winners deemed it appropriate for them to address courteous appeals to Pope Paul VI, stressing the urgence of the problem and offering him "the best of our professional capacities and endeavors" in helping him reach a decision on the birth-control question.

These unprecedented appeals reflect vividly the conviction of scientists and scholars of every faith and nation that the danger of uncontrolled population growth is one of the greatest now facing mankind and is second only to that of global nuclear warfare. The Nobel prize winners were aware that the Pope had appointed a committee of some sixty experts in many disciplines to study the whole problem in depth. This afforded them an excellent opportunity to urge the Church to reconsider its stand upon this matter along with the courteous proffer of their professional assistance.

Accordingly on March 18, 1965, both groups sent their appeals. The first group, consisting of forty-two British and European scientists and men of letters, was led by Dr. Peter Brian Medawar, a biologist who directs the National Institute for Medical Research in London. The second group, composed of thirty-six American Nobel laureates, one Argentinian, and two Australians, was under the leadership of Dr. E. L. Tatum, a biologist with Rockefeller University.

The two appeals were forwarded to the Vatican through the Most Rev. Hyginus Eugene Cardinale, apostolic delegate in Britain. Archbishop Cardinale had been chief of protocol at the Vatican during the pontificate of Pope John XXIII. Born in Italy, he had spent much time in the United States before his family returned to Rome.

The receipt of both letters was acknowledged by Amleto G. Cardinal Cicognani, secretary of state. He wrote that the Pope had been moved by the interest shown by such a body of men of letters and science. The letters, he reported, were referred to the Special Commission for the Study of Problems Relating to Population, Family, and Birth Control.

THE APPEAL OF FORTY-TWO BRITISH AND EUROPEAN NOBEL PRIZE WINNERS

His Holiness
Pope Paul VI
Vatican City
Rome, Italy

Your Holiness,

We, the undersigned Nobel laureates, are conscious of the great responsibility borne by Your Holiness in appraising and acting upon the advice offered by the commission you have appointed to study the problems of population and fertility control. Because of the profound bearing of your decision on human welfare and happiness, now and for many years to come, we urge you to give due weight to the ever-growing opinion which contends:

That the uncontrolled growth of population is a major evil of present times;

That unwanted children are a source of unhappiness, privation, and distress; and—

That parents should be able to exercise the right to have, so far as possible, only that number of children which can be cared for and cherished.

Lord Adrian, physiologist, Britain
Patrick Maynard Stuart Blackett, physicist, Britain
Max Born, physicist, German Federal Republic
Daniel Bovet, physiologist, Italy
Lord Boyd-Orr, physiologist, Britain
Sir Lawrence Bragg, physicist, Britain
Sir James Chadwick, physicist, Britain
Ernst Boris Chain, biochemist, Britain
Sir Henry Hallett Dale, scientist, Britain
Sir Howard Florey, pathologist, Britain
Werner Forssmann, surgeon, German Federal Republic
Otto Hahn, radiologist, German Federal Republic
Werner Heisenberg, physicist, German Federal Republic
Walter Rudolf Hess, physiologist, Switzerland
Jaroslav Heyrovsky, chemist, Czechoslovakia
Alan Lloyd Hodgkin, physiologist, Britain
Dorothy Crowfoot Hodgkin, crystallographer, Britain
Andrew Fleming Huxley, physiologist, Britain
Hans Daniel Jensen, physicist, German Federal Republic
Paul Karrer, chemist, Switzerland

John Cowdery Kendrew, biophysicist, Britain
Sir Hans Krebs, biochemist, Britain
Halldor Laxness, novelist, Iceland
Archer John Porter Martin, chemist, Britain
Peter Brian Medawar, biologist, Britain
Giullo Natta, chemist, Italy
Max Ferdinand Perutz, biochemist, Britain
Cecil Frank Powell, physicist, Britain
Salvatore Quasimodo, poet, Italy
Sir C. V. Raman, physicist, India
Tadeus Reichstein, chemist, Switzerland
Sir Robert Robinson, chemist, Britain
Earl Russell, philosopher, Britain
Frederick Sanger, biochemist, Britain
Theodor Svedberg, chemist, Sweden
Richard Laurence Millington Synge, biochemist, Britain
Arne Wilhelm Tiselius, chemist, Sweden
Hugo Theorell, biochemist, Sweden
Sir George Paget Thomson, physicist, Britain
Lord Todd, chemist, Britain
Maurice Hugh Frederick Wilkins, biologist, Britain
Karl Zeigler, chemist, German Federal Republic

THE APPEAL OF THIRTY-SIX AMERICAN, ONE ARGENTINIAN, AND TWO
AUSTRALIAN NOBEL PRIZE WINNERS

His Holiness
Pope Paul VI
Vatican City
Rome, Italy

Your Holiness,

We, the undersigned Nobel laureates, are deeply conscious of the immense burden of responsibility resting on the shoulders of Your Holiness in acting on the information and analyses of the commission you have designated to study the subject of population and fertility control. We extend our prayers and sympathies to Your Holiness and to the commission in this trying period leading to decisions that will affect the course of history, for all time and for all human beings, regardless of their religion.

Sensitive as all thoughtful men and women must be to the ethical context in which marriage and the family should be viewed, we are increasingly impressed by the emerging consensus about the goals of family planning—namely, to assure each new infant the birthright of a warm welcome in a loving home, with a healthy opportunity for education, employment, and fulfillment. The pressures of population growth now add a new moral imperative to the thoughtful consideration of family size.

In recognition of the gravity of the issue and the inevitable world-wide consequences of your action on it, we wish to express to Your Holiness the hope that any decisions will be the fruit of the most profound and searching studies. To this end, we wish to offer Your Holiness the best of our professional capacities and endeavors.

John Bardeen, physicist
Konrad E. Bloch, biochemist
Felix Bloch, physicist
Walter H. Brattain, physicist
Melvin Calvin, chemist
Owen Chamberlain, physicist
Andre Cournand, physician

Edward A. Doisy, physiologist
Vincent Du Vigneaud, chemist
John F. Enders, bacteriologist
Philip S. Hench, physician
Robert Hofstadter, physicist
Edward C. Kendall, chemist
Arthur Kornberg, chemist

Willis E. Lamb, physicist
Joshua Lederberg, geneticist
Tsung Dao Lee, physicist
Willard F. Libby, chemist
Fritz Albert Lipmann, biochemist
Maria Goeppert-Meyer, physicist
William P. Murphy, physician
John H. Northrop, chemist
Linus C. Pauling, chemist
Edward Mills Purcell, physicist
Isidor Isaac Rabi, physicist
Dickinson W. Richards, Jr.,
    physician
Frederick Chapman Robbins,
    physician

Emilio Segre, physicist
William Schockley, physicist
Wendell M. Stanley, biochemist
Albert Szent-Györgyi, biochemist
Edward L. Tatum, biologist
Harold C. Urey, chemist
Selman A. Waksman, physiologist
James D. Watson, biologist
Thomas H. Weller, physiologist
Sir Frank Macfarlane Burnet,
    pathologist, Australia
Sir John Carew Eccles, physiologist,
    Australia
Bernardo Albert Houssay,
    physiologist, Argentina

With the growth of the ecumenical spirit the members of different religious faiths are engaging with ever-increasing frequency in dialogue on matters of common interest and concern. Topics of a moral character are as relevant as those of a dogmatic nature and are frequently more divisive. Hence what could be more appropriate than for leaders of different faiths to discuss the burning issue of birth control in its moral, religious, and biblical aspects?

Accordingly Rev. Dr. John C. Bennett, president of Union Theological Seminary and a noted ecumenist, thought a service could be rendered by addressing to Pope Paul VI a statement reflecting the thought of leading churchmen as well as of scientists on responsible parenthood and the regulation of births. Since the matter involves a knowledge of the new findings of science, the thought of scientists would also be most relevant.

Accordingly Dr. Bennett and Dr. Edward L. Tatum sent to about one hundred theologians and scientists a statement for submission to Pope Paul VI. They were gratified to have eighty-five individuals respond promptly and affirmatively. On June 2, 1966, the document was sent to Rome and on June 27 its receipt was acknowledged by Monsignor Angelo Dell' Aqua of the Papal Office of Secretary of State.

Writing to Dr. Bennett, the prelate said: "The statement, 'The Moral Imperatives for Regulating Birth,' which you so kindly forwarded, has been presented to His Holiness in accordance with your kind request. You and Dr. Edward L. Tatum of the Rockefeller University will surely be pleased to learn that this statement has been referred to the commission charged with the responsibility of making a study in depth of this question."

THE MORAL IMPERATIVES FOR REGULATING BIRTH
A STATEMENT OF EIGHTY-FIVE RELIGIOUS LEADERS, THEOLOGIANS, AND SCIENTISTS FOR THE CONSIDERATION OF HIS HOLINESS, POPE PAUL VI
JUNE 2, 1966

The purpose of this statement is to express our heartfelt appreciation of the sensitive position on responsible parenthood and concern for problems of population growth reflected in the pastoral constitution on *The Church in the Modern World,* and to transmit our conviction that future generations will hold today's leaders morally responsible if we fail to recognize and deal with the world population crisis while it is still manageable on the basis of free conscience and free choice.

We know you are keenly aware of the many millions of your fellow men who are woefully malnourished or actually starving, and we feel sure you recognize, also, that despite man's ingenuity, the mounting pressures of population on world resources may subject future generations to hardships and miseries on a scale hitherto unknown. With full respect for the moral heritage of the traditional Catholic ethic on fertility control, we are profoundly convinced that a new moral consensus must be achieved among leaders of all major faiths, and that man's responsibility to the next generation includes a primary duty to limit that generation's size. It is the mark of great religions and the obligation of great leaders to recognize that changing conditions demand changing applications of unchanging moral values.

There are two moral elements of the matter, as we assess it, which must be joined and balanced in the conscience of modern man: First is the parental obligation of every couple to decide, with reverence for life, the number and spacing of its children, so that each family member may have the best prospect for health, vocation, and fulfillment. Second is the emerging social responsibility of each couple to reasonably limit family size as an essential step toward assuring that no man has too little of life's requirements and blessings because an excess of people requires too much.

It is paradoxical that so many problems confronting mankind today are the result of scientific progress in curbing one of our most ancient and formidable enemies—disease.

For most of human history, survival against such enemies required man to exercise his fertility most abundantly, so that total births exceeded—or at least equalled—total deaths. It was therefore morally imperative to encourage fertility and discourage the avoidance of pregnancy. But in our time many causes of early death have been finally overcome. For more than two centuries, human numbers have been growing with unprecedented, accelerating swiftness—the rate of growth has doubled in the past two decades alone. Today man's future is threatened less by rampant disease than by unbridled reproduction. Therefore, if future generations are to enjoy the quality of life made possible through the advances of science, our new moral imperative must call for the conscientious regulation of fertility.

The population dilemma, from which no individual is exempt, is equalled in magnitude only by the opportunity today's leaders share to influence its outcome for good or ill. If we achieve an affirmative moral consensus on this issue, those who follow will surely give thanks. If we fail, our conscience must bear the burden of their mounting hardships and the tragic loss of freedom and opportunity which we could have spared them. Our moral outlook must creatively confront these prospects of the future while remaining firmly rooted in the tested ethics of the past. Today your participation in the forging of a new consensus on this vital matter is essential for all mankind.

Dr. James Luther Adams
Professor of Christian Ethics
Harvard Divinity School
Harvard University
Cambridge, Massachusetts

Lord Edgar Douglas Adrian
Baron of Cambridge
Trinity College
Cambridge University
Cambridge, England

Bishop Hobart Amstutz
Methodist Church in Pakistan
74 Garden Road
P.O. Box 7254
Karachi 3, West Pakistan

Rev. Roland Bainton
Professor Emeritus of Ecclesiastical
  History
Yale Divinity School
409 Prospect Street
New Haven, Connecticut

Right Rev. Sante U. Barbieri
Casilla 5296, Correo Central
Buenos Aires, Argentina

Dr. John Bardeen
Professor of Physics and Electrical
  Engineering
University of Illinois
Urbana, Illinois

Dr. Norman J. Baugher
General Secretary
Church of the Brethren
Elgin, Illinois

Right Rev. Stephen F. Bayne, Jr.
Director of Overseas Department
Executive Council of the Episcopal
  Church
815 Second Avenue
New York, New York

Dr. Waldo Beach
Professor of Christian Ethics
Director of Graduate Studies in
  Religion
Duke University
Durham, North Carolina

Dr. John C. Bennett
President
Union Theological Seminary
Broadway at 120th Street
New York, New York

Rev. Dr. Hendrijus Berkhof
Professor of Theology
Leyden University
Julianalaan 18,
Oegstgeest, Netherlands

Bishop John D. Bright
Presiding Bishop of the First
  District
African Methodist Episcopal
  Church
6608 Lincoln Drive
Philadelphia, Pennsylvania

Dr. Robert McAfee Brown
Special Programs in Humanities
Stanford University
Stanford, California

Sir F. Macfarlane Burnet
Walter and Eliza Hall Institute
Royal Melbourne Hospital
Melbourne, Australia

Dr. K. A. Busia
Ghana University
Accra, Ghana

Adolf Friedrich Johann Butenandt
President, Max Planck Society
Director, Max Planck Institute for
  Biochemistry
Berlin University
Berlin, Germany

Dr. Alford Carleton
Executive Vice President
United Church Board for World
  Ministries
475 Riverside Drive
New York, New York

Dr. Ernst Boris Chain
Professor of Biochemistry
Imperial College of Science
Imperial Institute Road
London S.W. 7, England

Rev. J. Russell Chandran, Principal
The United Theological College
17 Miller's Road
Bangalore 6, India

Dr. Ivy Chou
Methodist Theological School
Sibu, Sarawak, Borneo

Dr. Harvey Cox
Associate Professor of Church and
  Society
The Divinity School
Harvard University
Cambridge, Massachusetts

Francis Harry Compton Crick
Institute of Molecular Biology
Cambridge University
Cambridge, England

Rev. Marion de Velder
Stated Clerk
Reformed Church in America

475 Riverside Drive
New York, New York

Dr. André Dumas
Professor of Ethics at the Faculty
of Theology
Paris, France

Dr. John F. Enders
Professor of Bacteriology and Im-
munology
Children's Hospital
Harvard Medical School
Cambridge, Massachusetts

Mrs. Sylvia Fernando
Vice President, All-Ceylon Women's
Conference
23/5 Horton Place
Colombo 7, Ceylon

Rev. Dr. A. Dale Fiers
Executive Secretary
International Convention of Chris-
tian Churches
222 South Downey Avenue
Indianapolis, Indiana

Professor George W. Forrell
Director, School of Religion
University of Iowa
Iowa City, Iowa

Dr. Franklin Clark Fry, President
Lutheran Church in America
231 Madison Avenue
New York, New York

Mrs. Goh Kok Kee
Chairman, East Asian Christian
Conference Consultation
10 Kay Siang Road
Singapore 10, Malaysia

Dr. Norman Goodall
Greensleeves, Benson
Oxford, England

Dr. James Gustafson
Professor of Christian Ethics

Yale Divinity School
409 Prospect Street
New Haven, Connecticut

Dr. Ben M. Herbster, President
United Church of Christ
297 Park Avenue South
New York, New York

Dr. Irene Ighodaro
Ibadan, Nigeria

Dr. Martin Luther King, Jr.
Co-Pastor, Ebenezer Baptist Church
President, Southern Christian Lead-
ership Conference
Atlanta, Georgia

Dr. Polykarp Kusch
Professor of Physics
Columbia University
New York, New York

Dr. William Lazareth, Dean
Philadelphia Lutheran Seminary
Philadelphia 19, Pennsylvania

Dr. Paul Lehmann
Professor of Systematic Theology
Union Theological Seminary
606 West 122nd Street
New York, New York

Bishop Robert F. Lundy
Methodist Church Malaysia and
Singapore
Box 483
Singapore 6, Malaysia

Dr. Duke McCall, President
The Southern Baptist Theological
Seminary
2825 Lexington Road
Louisville, Kentucky

Dr. Martin E. Marty
Chairman of the History of Chris-
tianity
University of Chicago
Divinity School
Chicago, Illinois

Bishop James K. Mathews
The Methodist Church
581 Boylston Street
Boston, Massachusetts

Dr. Samuel H. Miller
Dean of the Divinity School
Harvard University
Cambridge, Massachusetts

Dean Walter G. Muelder
Boston University School of Theology
745 Commonwealth Avenue
Boston, Massachusetts

Rev. Richard Neuhaus
Church of St. John the Evangelist
195 Mauger Street
Brooklyn, New York

Dr. Reinhold Niebuhr
Professor Emeritus
Union Theological Seminary
404 Riverside Drive
New York, New York

Dr. Shubert Ogden
Associate Professor of Theology
Perkins School of Theology
Southern Methodist University
Dallas, Texas

Dr. Linus C. Pauling
Research Professor
Center for the Study of Democratic
   Institutions
Box 4068
Santa Barbara, California

Mrs. Asuncion Perez
Philippine Wesleyan University
1648 Taft Avenue
Manila, Philippines

Rev. Harvey L. Perkins
The Methodist Church
511 Kent Street
Sydney, Australia

Rev. Canon Ronald Preston
Canon Residentiary of Manchester
   Cathedral
The Cathedral
Manchester 3, England

Dr. Jacob S. Quiambao
Executive Director
Association of Theological Schools
   Southeast Asia
Chairman, Department of Sociology
   and Social Ethics
P.O. Box 841
1648 Taft Avenue
Manila, Philippines

Dr. Paul Ramsey
Harrington Spear Paine Professor
   of Religion
Princeton University
Princeton, New Jersey

Right Rev. Chandu Ray
Bishop's House
P.O. Box 330
Karachi, Pakistan

Rev. Dr. Heinz G. Renkewitz
Evangelical Church
Eichwaldsfeld Arnoldshain/Ts,
   Germany

Dr. Dickinson W. Richards
Lambert Professor of Medicine,
   Emeritus
Columbia University College of
   Physicians and Surgeons
630 West 168th Street
New York, New York

Dr. Cyril C. Richardson
Dean of Graduate Studies
Union Theological Seminary
3041 Broadway
New York, New York

Mr. Jackie Robinson
United Church Men

475 Riverside Drive
New York, New York

Right Rev. Henry Knox Sherrill
Presiding Bishop of Protestant Episcopal Church
Boxford, Massachusetts

Dr. Roger L. Shinn
Dean of Instruction
Professor of Applied Christianity
Union Theological Seminary
3041 Broadway
New York, New York

Dr. William Shockley
Professor of Engineering Science
Stanford Electronics Laboratory
Stanford University
Palo Alto, California

Dr. Joseph Sittler
Professor of Theology
Chicago Lutheran Theological Seminary
University of Chicago
Chicago, Illinois

Rev. Virgil A. Sly, President
United Chistian Missionary Society
222 South Downey Avenue
Indianapolis, Indiana

Dr. Wendell M. Stanley
Professor of Molecular Biology
Professor of Biochemistry
Director of the Virus Laboratory
Chairman, Department of Virology

University of California
Berkeley, California

Pastor Ingmar Stoltz
c/o Reverend Aoke Castlund
Jacobsbergsgatan 19
Stockholm, Sweden

Mrs. K. I. Suzuki
Executive Secretary
Christian Home and Family Life

and Women's Committee
National Christian Council
2, h-chome, Ginza
Tokyo, Japan

Dr. Albert Szent-Györgyi
Director of Research
Institute for Muscle Research
Marine Biological Laboratories
P.O. Box 187
Woods Hole, Massachusetts

Dr. Edward L. Tatum
Professor of Biochemical Genetics
Rockefeller University
66th Street and York Avenue
Flexner Hall, Room 116-118
New York, New York

Dr. Hugo Theorell
Professor of Medicine and Physiology
Caroline Institute
Stockholm, Sweden

Most Rev. Juhanon Mar Thoma, Metropolitan
Mar Thoma Syrian Church of Malabar
The Metropolitan's House
Tiruvalla, Travancore (Kerala), India

Dr. George F. Thomas
Moses Taylor Pyne Professor of Religion
Princeton University
Princeton, New Jersey

Dr. M. M. Thomas
Christian Institute for the Study of Religion and Society
Box 1504
17, Millers Road
Bangalore 6, India

Dr. Arne Wilhelm Kaurin Tiselius
Professor of Biochemistry
University of Uppsala
Uppsala, Sweden

Dr. Charles H. Townes, Provost
Massachusetts Institute of Technology
Cambridge, Massachusetts

Dr. Harold C. Urey
Professor of Chemistry
University of California, San Diego
La Jolla, California

Dr. Artturi Ilmari Virtanen
Director of the Biochemical Institute
Helsinki University
Helsinki, Finland

Dr. Klaus Von Bismarck
Westdeutscher Rundfunk
Koeln Wallrafplatz 5, Germany

Dr. Selman A. Waksman
Professor of Microbiology
Director of Institute of Microbiology
Rutgers University
New Brunswick, New Jersey

Right Rev. Alwyn Keith Warren
Bishop of Christchurch
Bishopscourt, 100 Park Terrace
Christchurch, New Zealand

Rev. Canon Max Alexander Cunningham Warren
Sub-Dean and Canon of Westminster
3 Little Cloister
Westminster S.W. 1, England

Bishop Hazen G. Werner
Bishop of Hong Kong and Taiwan
Chairman, World Family Life Committee of Methodist Church
777 United Nations Plaza
New York, New York

Rev. Dr. M. Moran Weston
St. Philip's Protestant Episcopal Church
133rd Street and 7th Avenue
New York, New York

Dr. Whang Kyoung Koh, President
Seoul Women's College
Kong-Duck Ni, No-Hae Myun
Kyonggido, Seoul, Korea

Professor Daniel Williams
430 Canner Street
New Haven, Connecticut

Professor George Williams
Hollis Professor of Divinity
Harvard University Divinity School
Cambridge, Massachusetts

18

BIRTH CONTROL
AND THE CATHOLIC CHURCH

by Clare Boothe Luce

A former representative of Connecticut in the U. S. Congress, Mrs. Luce also served as U. S. Ambassador to Italy. The author of many successful and notable plays, she has been a newspaper columnist and the associate editor of *Vanity Fair*. She has contributed articles and fiction to magazines of national circulation and has received honorary LL.D. degrees from several of our leading universities.

Some time ago I received a letter, from a non-Catholic reader, on the subject of birth control and the Catholic Church. The writer, a married woman with several children, said she had two good Catholic friends, one of whom had three children and was "taking the pill" with the permission of her confessor; the other friend, pregnant for the fourth time, "although she had been using the rhythm method," said *her* priest insisted that birth control by any other means was a mortal sin. What, this correspondent wanted to know, was the real position of the Church? She also wanted me to tell her whether or not I agreed with the Church's position.

The Church is, and has been for a long time, responsive to all the valid arguments for birth control. It enlarges the freedom of woman and gives scope to the love of man and wife. It prevents the evil and danger of abortion. Spacing pregnancies strengthens the family—the basic unit of society—since it permits parents to plan thoughtfully for the education and rearing of children. And birth control offers a long-range hope for solutions of the problem of world overpopulation and the corollary problem of world hunger.

The Church teaches that parents bear the responsibility, before God, of deciding on the number of children they are able to rear and educate. But the Church does not believe married couples have the right, before God, to choose among existing birth-control methods. It maintains that any agent of a chemical or mechanical nature that destroys or obstructs life-giving sperm or aborts life-giving ovum is against the natural law, and therefore that the use of such an agent is immoral.

Sexual continence was the only form of birth control Catholics were permitted to practice licitly, until the scientific discovery of the natural, and more or less regular, period of infertility in woman's menstrual cycle. In 1930, in his encyclical *Casti Connubii* (Christian Marriage), Pope Pius XI authorized Catholics to use the rhythm method. This permits those Catholics who, for sound and moral reasons, wish to space pregnancies to confine marital intercourse to the wife's infertile periods.

What the Church has not authorized, and what it has up to now officially banned, is use of the pill and the loop (the intrauterine coil), etc., on the grounds that these are unnatural birth-control agents.

It would seem, then, that my correspondent's friend who was taking the pill and her confessor who had given her permission to do so were indeed sinners in the eyes of the Church. But before we leap to this harsh judgment, let us review some recent catholic history.

During the second session of Vatican Council II (1963), the issue of the theology of marriage began to command the bishops' attention. In the spring of 1964, Pope Paul VI announced the formation of a Papal Commission for the Study of Population, the Family, and Births. The mandate of the commission gave it full freedom. The action was timely; except for control of nuclear weapons, world opinion considers no subject more important than birth control.

Many Catholics assumed (reasonably enough, it seems to me) that the Pope's having appointed such a deliberative body was ample evidence that the mind of the Church was open to the adoption of any new birth-control method that was not unnatural—as, most certainly, abortion and sterilization are. Many Catholics also assumed (and again, it seems to me, reasonably enough) that, in reaching its conclusions on a matter dealing not only with the spiritual but with the physiological and biological nature of man, the Church would surely give weight to the views of doctors and scientists as well as to the opinions of theologians.

The character of the commission fortified this assumption. Its sixty members, representing many countries, included theologians and prelates of high rank, doctors, scientists, sociologists, demographers, and married couples.

In the spring of 1966, to broaden the basis of opinion, the commission was enlarged by the addition of sixteen bishops, including some cardinals. In view of the extraordinary delicacy, complexity, and controversiality of the subject, members of the commission were pledged to keep their deliberations secret from the press and the public. However, very large and mixed commissions that meet over extended periods are eventually the source of rumors, more or less well founded. The Vatican's commission proved to be no exception. What eventually leaked out was (a) a majority of the commission members thought God's injunction to "replenish the earth," unlike many of His other commandments, was being obeyed so diligently that the earth was groaning under the burdens of replenishment; and (b) while the divine command is certainly still valid, God may not have intended to apply it to every single act of marital love; and (c) if (a) and (b) were the case, in human fertility, as in all else, moderation might well be hailed as a Christian virtue; and (d) it was not clear that means other than the highly uncertain rhythm method were beyond moral sanction.

As these rumors reached the ears of the faithful, many happily assumed that the pill would eventually be accepted as legitimate. This was not unreasonable. First, it seemed to many Catholics, especially in the United States, unthinkable that the conclusions of a majority of a great pontifical commission that had sat for years on a subject so vitally important—not only to millions of Catholic spouses but to everybody in the world—would be rejected by the Pontiff; and second, a number of prominent Catholic doctors and scientists had been publicly insisting for some time that the pill could be scientifically classified as a natural means of birth control.

Many Catholics (including some priests), knowing quite well that, until the Pope spoke definitively about the commission's report, the birth control question was by no means settled, nevertheless permitted themselves to be guided by a traditional doctrinal rule—namely, that a doubt about the moral law favors the freedom of conscience. Some confessors argued that the Church *was* in a state of doubt, because of the reliably reported division of opinion within the commission.

The priest who allowed the mother of three to use the pill certainly must have believed that until the Pope spoke, the Church's seeming state of doubt permitted him to use his own discretion.

At long last, on June 28, 1966, the results of the commission's work were laid on the Pope's desk—an 800-page document, containing both a majority and a minority report. For four months nothing happened. As the summer wore away, the only news was that the Pontiff was poring over the report, whose text and conclusions were a closely guarded Vatican secret. (As of this writing, they remain so.) [1]

Then, in late October, the Pope made a speech to the Italian Society of Obstetrics and Gynecology. To the dismay of many in his audience and to the disappointment of millions of Catholics, he said that the Church's "traditional teaching"—that the only licit means of birth control for Catholics is the rhythm method—could *not* be considered to be "in a state of doubt."

Did this mean that he had rejected the recommendation of the majority of his commission? Was this his final word on the subject? Perhaps yes—because, referring to the commission in his speech, he said

[1] Editor's note. The majority and minority reports were "leaked" to the press and were published in full in *The National Catholic Reporter*, April 19, 1967. The report of the great majority of doctors, economists, demographers, sociologists, and theologians as well as a "substantial" majority of the bishops favored a liberalization of the Church's teaching that would permit any medically approved method of birth regulation other than sterilization and abortion.

that while it was "an ample and most versatile international commission" and had done "great work," at the same time "it seems to us that they [the commission's conclusions] cannot be considered definitive, for the reason that they present grave implications regarding other questions of the doctrinal, pastoral, and social order, which cannot be isolated or put aside." And "they [the inplications] demand a logical consideration in the context of the question under study."

But then again, perhaps no: In the same speech, the Pope said that he knew the world awaited his "decisive word" and that birth control was "a most vast and delicate subject," so he could not give his "decisive word in this circumstance." Finally, he added that his "decisive word" would be delayed until he had given the matter a good deal more thought. "I must defer it [his decision on the report] still for some time."

It seems clear that the Pope has not made up his mind whether to accept or reject the majority report, in whole or in part; that he is waiting until he has more information from scientists or receives more proof from his theologians or is better informed about the bishops' views. Meanwhile, he wants it understood that, for the present, "the old order standeth."

What lies at the bottom of the Pontiff's painful indecision? Early in November, the authoritative Vatican journal, *L'Osservatore Romano*, published an editorial on the Church's present position on birth control that casts some—but not much—light on this question.

"One notes," the editorial said, "that an ever-growing propaganda, which tends to instill the belief that without controlled limitation of births, within a few years, the human species will die of hunger, comes to be put forward as a definitive and incontestable argument [for certain birth-control methods up to now banned by the Church]." The editorial reminds its readers that the traditional position—that of Pius XII especially—was that the *only* moral solution to the overpopulation problem would be "mastery of self by man." In other words, continence, absolute or periodic, as with the rhythm method.

The situation in the Vatican may, then, be this: The commission's majority report may reflect a conviction that the threat of overpopulation has created a new and fearful world situation that transcends traditional Catholic morality on birth control. And the Pope must be cruelly aware that his rejection of this report would be viewed as a regressive action by most of the world's political, scientific, and religious leaders, and quite possibly by a great number of communicants. On the other hand, there is the great and grave question of the continuity of Catholic tradition—and the consistency, as it were, of papal authority. How can a subsequent pope deny a morality a previous pope seemed to have affirmed?

If this *is* the spiritual and intellectual dilemma in which Pope Paul finds himself, it is, indeed, an agonizing one. For, however resolved, it is fraught with implications for the Church and for society.

Meanwhile, the situation in the Catholic world, unhappily, is this: Whether or not the Pope is in doubt, much of the Catholic world believes he is. And human nature being what it is, in the matter of the pill, unknown numbers of Catholics will continue to give themselves the benefit of the doubt.

As for my own view, I hope with all my mind and heart that Pope Paul will yet receive enough new evidence from scientists and support from bishops and theologians to enable him to accept the findings of the majority of his commission.

There are many reasons I hope this, but two will suffice: First, *L'Osservatore Romano* to the contrary, the scientific warnings of the threat of overpopulation are not "propaganda." These warnings are pouring in from every government and scientific source in the world that has competence in fields of agriculture and demography.

During the commission's three years of life, enough babies were born to populate 100 cities the size of Rome. If the daily diet enjoyed by Romans today can be considered anywhere near what human beings need to maintain health, most of these babies were born only to suffer chronic malnutrition. According to a recent report of the United Nations Committee on Multilateral Food Aid, "half the people in the world [*today*] are ill-fed" and "half the school-age children are so undernourished that their physical and mental growth is retarded." The UN report states that mortality among small children in developing countries is *some sixty times as great as in the advanced countries.* What makes this situation even more desperate is that millions of *parents* are so poorly nourished that they do not have the physical strength to "serve effectively the urgent demands of industrialization and economic development." Finally, the UN experts report that if the present birth rates continue, fifteen years from now there will be one billion more mouths to feed.

Technology and science, of course, can do vastly more—and should do more—to help alleviate this situation. But one thing science cannot do is enlarge earth space. President Johnson recently warned that the hour is coming "when all the acres of all the agriculturally productive nations" will not meet the food needs of the developing nations.

It seems to me that this is self-evident. It takes neither a scientist nor a theologian to figure out that *at some point the population of the world must be stabilized or regulated by birth control* unless we are willing to accept the only other alternative. This is to trust population control to that evil trinity of all our darkest history—war, pestilence, and famine. Whatever God's will for man may be, surely it is not that population is best controlled by starvation, disease, and nuclear holocaust.

Second, the rhythm method is not adapted to the use of the very people who need it most—for example, the pitifully poor and illiterate populations of the Catholic Latin-American countries. What agency will supply them with the millions of calendars, pencils, and erasers (no less the $25 electric "lady clocks," so popular with wealthy Catholics in this country) initially needed to make the rhythm method work? What vast corps of doctors will then instruct them in the use of these calendars? And what eloquent priests will infuse them with the physical and spiritual strength to practice checked-off love and clocked-out continence?

Even educated Catholics in our affluent society find the rhythm method difficult. A Catholic woman, bearing her fifth child, recently wrote to me: "Why doesn't somebody tell the Church that if it wants rhythm to work, it should ban double beds and even grant indulgences for sleeping in separate rooms? . . . The next time, I'm just not going to talk to my confessor. My landlord has already talked to me."

I share what, according to rumor, is the majority view in the papal commission's report: Any physically harmless birth-control means, short of sterilization (which is sexual suicide) and abortion (which is self-violence and infanticide) should be accepted by the Church.

How will the problem be solved? No one knows. But those who know Pope Paul know that he combines two virtues rarely found together—courage and consummate prudence. Consequently, many Catholics, myself included, believe he will follow the course of courage, which is likewise the course of prudence. He will move forward with the movement of history and with the progress of moral-scientific thought, in conformity with Catholic tradition, which is a tradition of progress. The authority of the papacy will be more secure for this progress.

19

RESPECT FOR CONSCIENCE IN A PLURALISTIC SOCIETY

by John A. O'Brien

Every day witnesses the arrival of about 260,000 more babies upon a planet whose skyrocketing population presents a problem and a threat second only to that of nuclear war on a global scale. One way of meeting that problem is, in part, by stressing parental responsibility to regulate the number of offspring.

There is, however, another fact, so far-reaching in its implications that it alone should enable us to end the battle over birth control and to work constructively together to solve the population problem both at home and abroad. This fact is that we live in a pluralistic society whose members are characterized by the widest divergence of religious faiths. With more than 300 denominations in our midst, it is obvious that we must learn not only to live together but also to respect scrupulously the consciences of others and work together for the common good.

The consequence of such religious pluralism is that no one group may impose its distinctive creedal or moral viewpoint through the clenched fist of legislative fiat or government directive upon those of other faiths. The attempt to do so is rightly resented as intolerable arrogance; it is an utterly unwarranted infringement on the constitutional rights of others and is doomed to failure. Its only result is the generation of bad blood, bitterness, hatred, and strife.

In view of the not infrequent violations of the principle of religious liberty for each individual and group in a pluralistic community, it may seem strange to Catholics and non-Catholics alike that this is the clear teaching of the Catholic Church as expressed through its supreme authority. In an address to the Roman Rota, October 6, 1946, Pope Pius XII said:

"The increasingly frequent contacts between different religious professions, mingled indiscriminately within the same union, have caused civil authorities to follow the principles of tolerance and liberty of conscience. In fact, there is a political tolerance, a civil tolerance, a social tolerance, in regard to adherents of other religious beliefs, which, in circumstances such as these, is a moral duty for Catholics." Hence Catholics are bound in conscience to exercise civil and religious tolerance and to respect the constitutional rights of others.

This principle was further confirmed and amplified in the Pontiff's discourse, *Religion in the Community of Nations,* addressed to the Convention of Italian Catholic Jurists, December 6, 1953. Here the Pope points out that God Himself, though infinitely powerful, does not interfere with human freedom in order to repress error or moral deviation. He cites the parable of the cockle wherein Christ gives the following advice: Let the cockle grow in the field of the world together with the good seed in view of the harvest.

Then the Pontiff concludes: "The duty of repressing moral and religious error cannot therefore be an ultimate norm of action. It must be subordinate to higher and more general norms." In other words, religious error is to be tolerated in the modern state "in order to promote a greater good"—the peace and order of society.

The implementation of this principle surely demands that Catholics and non-Catholics meet around a table to discuss the population problem, analyze their points of agreement and difference, and solve the problem in a way that will respect the consciences of all. This will require patience, a sympathetic understanding of the other's viewpoint, and a realization that neither side can force its distinctive view upon the other.

"We Catholics," said Cardinal Cushing of Boston, "must recognize the rights of Protestants to their own conscientious beliefs, and vice versa. I, as a Catholic, have absolutely no right in my thinking to foist, through legislation or through any other means, any doctrine of my Church upon others . . . other people have their own conscientious beliefs. I am obligated to respect them, and vice versa."

Cardinal Bea, president of the Secretariat for Promoting Christian Unity, was, after the Pope, probably the most highly esteemed prelate at the recent Council. In an address at Rome's Pro Deo University in January 1963 to 500 persons from sixty-nine nations and of twenty-one faiths, including Jews, Moslems, Buddhists, and Taoists, the cardinal declared that the love of truth, practiced in charity, is the road to harmony among individuals and groups. He characterized the wars of religion of past centuries as "another error of the misunderstood love of truth. During those wars men tried to impose by force and in the name of truth certain convictions on other men, forgetting the no less fundamental value of . . . man's freedom. This freedom means man's right to dispose freely of his own destiny according to his own conscience."

Reflecting this newly recognized need for the religious freedom of each group in a pluralistic society, four priest-professors at Laval University in Quebec have called for legislative action to permit civil marriages and the taking of a solemn declaration instead of an oath on the Bible in civil courts. "By virtue of the respect due to the liberty of conscience in a pluralistic society," they said, "individuals and groups who do not share the religious feelings of almost all the population have a right to have their legitimate demands respected."

It will help Catholics to understand the good faith and the sincere and deep moral convictions of their non-Catholic neighbors if they realize that a revolution has taken place in their ethical thinking on birth regulation since 1931. In that year the Federal Council of Churches of Christ in America endorsed contraceptive methods of birth control. Since then most large Protestant denominations, including the Episcopal Church, have approved contraceptive birth control, lock, stock, and barrel, and in some cases have even declared it to be a religious duty.

Hence a new moral code on this subject has become integrated into the religious faith of most Protestants. Under the Constitution they have the right to practice their faith without let or hindrance. Any interference is rightly viewed as an infringement of their religious liberty guaranteed by the Constitution.

The revolution in the ethical thinking of Protestants has occurred with such speed that many Catholics seem unaware that contraception is no longer in Protestant eyes an evil thing, but may be a good, virtuous, and even holy action, demanded by the changed conditions of modern life and commended by the vast majority of physicians. Furthermore, repeated surveys show that a majority of Protestant married couples in this country regard contraceptive birth control as thoroughly decent and moral, and are following this practice.

The failure to recognize this revolution in Protestant ethical and religious thought leaves not a few Catholics laboring under the erroneous impression that their views on contraception still reflect the moral consensus of virtually the whole Christian community. It is this cultural lag—the failure to appreciate the radical change in Protestant thinking —that partly explains their occasional recourse to the police power of the state to suppress contraceptive birth-control practices, advertising, and clinics. It is also related to opposition to the repeal of anti-birth-control laws in some states.

The radical, profound, and sweeping change which has occurred in the Protestant cultural climate and religious viewpoint within one generation is dramatically illustrated by two instances. In 1917 Margaret Sanger was found guilty by a court and sentenced for providing contraceptive birth-control information at a birth-control clinic. In 1949 she was awarded an honorary degree from Smith College as "a leader in world-wide study of population problems and a pioneer in the American birth-control movement." Thus in the brief span of thirty-two years the pendulum has swung full length.

It is easy for a religious organization that once had its dogmas anchored in the thought, practice, usages, social institutions, and mores of society to imagine that it still enjoys such comfortable backing. It comes as something of a jolt and a rude awakening to realize that much of the old support in the moral consensus of the American community has crumbled away. That realization is necessary, however, if one is to appreciate the good faith and the integrity of conscience of those whose religious creed contains new and revolutionary elements.

It is a cultural lag which also lies behind the failure of the inhabitants of the underdeveloped countries to realize the importance of the radically changed conditions brought about by the introduction of modern health-care techniques. Accustomed to having four or five children reach adulthood, women gave birth to nearly twice that number. With infant mortality now virtually wiped out, they still continue to beget the customary number. The result is the spectacular upsurge of the population, flooded with new mouths to feed.

In a pluralistic society a group best shows its maturity not by general obstreperousness and "throwing its weight around," but by a sensitivity to the conscientious convictions and religious beliefs of others, even of small splinter groups. It is upon the development of such a social sensitivity that Catholic schools are now placing great stress.

This was evidenced by a resolution adopted at the close of the fifty-seventh annual convention of the National Catholic Educational Association on April 22, 1960. Catholic schools were urged to continue their efforts "to find increasingly effective ways of developing within their students a deep sense of social responsibility, and particularly of their responsibilities as Catholics within a pluralistic society."

How is such sensitivity to be achieved? Obviously by frank and friendly discussion with their non-Catholic neighbors on all matters affecting the welfare of the community. Only in this way can a pluralistic society maintain its health and vigor and be enabled to act constructively in solving its problems.

In stressing the beneficial effect interreligious activity would have on the social order, the nation, and world peace, Cardinal Cushing said: "We must work together on all levels which do not demand of us the denial of the faith we have. I'm all for Catholics being identified with Protestants and Jews and all others in every possible friendly and helpful way."

Speaking at a convocation at St. Catherine's College in St. Paul, Father Thomas Stransky, C.S.P., an American priest now working in Rome with the Secretariat for Promoting Christian Unity, stated that "the built-in logic of our times is making more real the truth that God created all men that they might live together in peace."

He pointed out that the Church's new willingness to listen to criticism from non-Catholics represents a great change of attitude. "This wasn't true fifty years ago," he continued. "We realize that the Holy Spirit can speak to us through Protestant mouths. All of us are giving glory to God by our attention to our separated brethren."

As part of the ecumenical movement to promote better understanding among all Christians, Catholics are urged to engage in friendly dialogues with their Protestant neighbors. The object is to perceive more clearly where we agree and where we disagree, and then to see how we can enlarge our areas of agreement and narrow those of our divergence. Surely the corollary of this is that they should meet to discuss the social problems which stem from our divergent religious creeds and moral codes.

In such conferences the laity should be well represented, for they have an important contribution to make. "Working together to make a better world," points out John Cogley, a staff member of the Center for the Study of Democratic Institutions, "would surely have ecumenical effects. The laity who are bound by ties of affection and genuine love to so many Protestants and who frequently even live in the same family with Christians of other faiths may have something important to contribute to the ecumenical movement: a kind of untutored understanding of the importance of Christian unity and feeling for brotherhood that does not come easily to professional churchmen, Protestant or Catholic, who spend so much of their lives in denominational isolation."

Out of the dialogues already held has emerged a finding of much significance: the difficulty of non-Catholics to understand the moral objection of Catholics to contraception. Catholics think that by the use of reason man can ascertain the Creator's purposes in the operation of nature and its laws, and that God makes known His purposes by certain structural arrangements.

But persons whose religious faith does not include the natural law concept or tradition are honestly unable to appreciate what Catholics regard as its cogency. Eminent Protestant churchmen and scholars, such as Reinhold Niebuhr, Bishop Fred Pierce Corson, Dean John C. Bennett are among those who have so testified. Protestants are thus committed to a different viewpoint, a different religious belief, and their sincerity cannot be questioned. An appreciation of this fact will help Catholics achieve that social sensitivity so indispensable for orderly and friendly community life in a pluralistic society.

Faith involves the free decision of the intellect and will. It cannot be coerced. Like other nations of the West, the United States is committed to the religious freedom of all men. So, too, is the Catholic Church. Its belief in universal religious freedom has as its theological basis the necessary freedom for the act of faith.

"In Catholic teaching," points out Monsignor John Tracy Ellis of the University of San Francisco, "there is nothing that supersedes a man's conscience in the acceptance or nonacceptance of the truths of faith. Nor is he ever compelled to recognize an allegiance or authority higher than his conscience." Hence those who act according to their conscience never incur blame in the eyes of God.

The frank recognition of the far-reaching implications of the fact that we are living in a pluralistic society does not mean an espousal of religious indifferentism, moral relativism, or a moral code divorced from the natural law and based solely upon subjective feelings and emotions. Neither does it mean that truth, either philosophic or religious, is to be determined by a majority vote. It simply means that citizens of divergent religious faiths can work together to solve the problems which constantly arise in modern community life.

Pope Pius XII repeatedly called upon Catholics throughout the world to co-operate with "all men of good will" in the achievement of great objectives on both a national and an international scale, which no single religious group could attain by going it alone. So frequent were his appeals for such co-operation that he could justly be called the Pope of Co-operation. His frequent appeals show how unwarranted is the action of so many Catholics in shying away from co-operation with their non-Catholic neighbors on even such projects as slum clearance and the promotion of civil rights.

Like his predecessor, Pope John XXIII has likewise appealed for such co-operation and joint action with such frequency and vigor as to both astonish and warm the heart of the world. Pope Paul VI has continued this policy of co-operation, and today the Church calls upon all her members throughout the world to support the United Nations and to help that organization in its struggle for peace, justice, and liberty.

In the UN are Communist countries which profess militant atheism and seek to remove God and every vestige of religion from the lives of their people. Because of the extreme divergences of religious viewpoint prevailing among the members of the United Nations, its deliberations begin with no prayer, and even the name of God is not mentioned. In the chapel in the United Nations Building in New York there is not a single religious symbol of any kind. Surely then if Catholics are called upon to support the United Nations and to work for its development and the extension of its influence throughout the world, they can sit down around a table with our Protestant, Jewish, and churchless friends and neighbors to discuss ways and means of solving the population problem.

The realization that the time has come when Catholics must recognize the revolutionary changes in modern life and thought is reflected in a recent editorial in the Jesuit-edited weekly, *America*. "Catholics," it says, "must make their fellow citizens realize: 1. the concern of Catholics about human problems everywhere; 2. their willingness to co-operate in searching for a truly humane and moral solution to these problems; 3. their determination to question any effort at stampeding the nation into some fixed policy in an area where we still have precious little hard knowledge. That area embraces the relationship between population growth and economic development."

A similarly constructive suggestion for effective co-operation was made by James O'Gara, managing editor of *Commonweal*. "Since the birth-control issue," he says, "is one of the most divisive in American life, on which a reasonable consensus is impossible, simple political prudence suggests that this matter be left to the nations concerned and to the conscientious convictions of their own people . . .

"In the present controversy over birth control and foreign aid, religious-minded men have allowed themselves to be sidetracked into a bitter and essentially pointless dispute that could have disastrous effects. This strikes me as an act of political folly which only obscures the central fact on which we could all agree: the urgent necessity of an expanded, long-term effort by all the nations of the West to enlarge productive capacity in the underdeveloped nations. Unless this is done, on a scale far beyond anything we have yet attempted, peace in our time is impossible, birth control or no."

Another constructive suggestion that points the way to effective action in helping the underdeveloped countries deal with their soaring population problems was made by Rev. James L. Vizzard, S.J., director of the Washington office of the National Catholic Rural Life Conference. Testifying on the Foreign Assistance Act of 1962 before the House Foreign Affairs committee, Father Vizzard said he does not think "we have faced up clearly and courageously to the practical implications for public policy of the deep split between conscientious citizens over what means, if any, may be used in dealing with apparently harmful population growth."

Archbishop Robert E. Lucey of San Antonio spelled out some of those practical implications in January 1967 when he informed Catholic members of the local antipoverty agency that they did not have a moral responsibility to oppose a funding request by the Planned Parenthood Federation. The city council had granted that organization permission to use city health clinics. Two persons dissented and filed a minority report, citing the danger of coercion, a stand similar to that taken by the U.S. bishops in November 1966.

Archbishop Lucey then sent a memorandum to James Kazin, president of the Economic Opportunities Development Corporation, explaining that its Catholic members had "no moral obligation to withhold contraceptive information and devices from a large number of fellow citizens who sincerely believe they have this right."

The archbishop also removed a common misconception. "Some of our fellow citizens," he said, "sincerely believe that the Catholic Church advocates irresponsible parenthood. They imagine that our motto is: 'The larger the family, the better for everybody.' This is not true."

In support of his stand, the archbishop quoted from the pastoral constitution on *The Church in the Modern World:* "Parents should regard as their proper mission the task of transmitting human life and educating those to whom it has been transmitted. They will fulfill their task with human and Christian responsibility."

All the members of the five Notre Dame Conferences on the Population Problem, sponsored by the Ford Foundation, were agreed that further intensive research covering the whole broad field of human reproduction was urgently needed and would lead to significant findings in a field long shrouded in mystery. Such research can profitably be conducted by medical schools, research foundations, and especially the National Institutes of Health.

Until these developments are achieved, however, we all can learn a lesson from the lowliest of God's creatures, the simple oyster. When a grain of sand enters its shell and sets up an irritation, it surrounds that grain with a secretion which transforms it into a shining pearl. Through understanding, good will, and brotherhood, we in America can transform the irritations inherent in a pluralistic society, with hundreds of different religious creeds, into the shining pearl of community peace. This is indeed a precious treasure. It is the pearl beyond all price.

We believe that people of intelligence and good will can find a way to preserve that peace through mutual concessions, without either the compromise of principle or the sacrifice of conscience. In this way we can make the American way of life a stimulating challenge, a source of intellectual and spiritual enrichment for our own people, and an inspiration to the peoples of other lands. This is the genius and the glory of America. This is the American dream, and, working together, we can make that dream come true.

20

A CRISIS IN HUMAN HISTORY

by John A. O'Brien

With hundreds of thousands of new inhabitants being placed each day upon our earth, chiefly in the underdeveloped countries, action is needed now. The crisis has already overtaken us. Millions of people are not only ill-fed but also are suffering the pangs of chronic hunger and slow starvation.

We are in a race between food supply and population increase and we are losing that race. "The time for rhetoric," President Johnson warns us, "has clearly passed. The time for concerted action is here . . . Every member of the world community now bears a direct responsibility to help bring our most basic human account into balance."

How can we achieve that balance? Only by regulating births can we control population growth. But here is the rub. Catholics are, at present, limited by the Church to continence, complete or periodic, to regulate births. Periodic continence, known as the rhythm method, is unfortunately not the most reliable and effective. The menstrual cycle of most women is so varied as to render the sterile or "safe" period difficult to predict with accuracy.

True, permission to use the pill for a limited time, not as a contraceptive but to achieve a regular menstrual cycle to render the rhythm method more effective, represents a forward step. But even with this improvement the method is far from a satisfactory solution. This was shown by the survey, conducted by Dr. John Cavanaugh, of women using the rhythm method. Despite earnest efforts to make the method work, the majority reported dissatisfaction with it.

Couples using this method have reported seven and eight pregnancies within nine and ten years. Despite their remarkable religious motivation and meticulous care, Dr. and Mrs. André de Bethune had nine children in eleven years. In the underdeveloped countries, where effective methods are most urgently needed, the rhythm method is impracticable because of the high rate of illiteracy.

The papal commission, on which there are gynecologists, demographers, physicians, and scientists, as well as theologians, has studied the subject with great care and has presented its 800-page report to the Pope. Unofficially the great majority of its members is reported to favor a liberalization of the present ruling. Indeed many are said to favor any medically approved method, short of sterilization and abortion.

Meanwhile there has been a marked advance in theological thinking on the subject. Thus all theologians now teach that, for any reasonable cause, the marriage partners may separate the sex act from its consequences by use of the infertile period. Furthermore, they teach that, though procreation is normally the purpose or end of marriage as an institution, it is not the goal or end of *every* conjugal act. There are many other rich interpersonal values, such as the fostering and deepening of mutual love and the shared joy with which man and woman become "one flesh," which can and should be obtained through the marriage relation, even though no pregnancy is achieved or even intended. It is the important distinction between marriage in its *totality* and in its *individual* acts or expressions.

Moreover, since it is universally agreed by all Catholics that, for any good reason, couples may separate the sex act from pregnancy by *temporal* interposition in the use of rhythm, theologians are now asking the Church's magisterium to reexamine the reasons why they may not accomplish the same end, and do it more effectively, by *medico-glandular* interposition (e.g., the pill) or *physical* interposition (e.g., condoms or diaphragms). Doesn't the rhythm method, they ask, use *time,* as measured by a calendar—and abetted by a thermometer—as a positive instrument to achieve the sex act without pregnancy?

What moral difference is there between it and the other physically harmless means prescribed by medical science? Isn't it just about the difference between Tweedledum and Tweedledee? Isn't it *natural,* not unnatural, for man to use his intelligence to achieve through medical science the most effective and harmless means of effectively spacing offspring? When a surgeon removes a cancer, isn't he interfering with *nature* but doing so for man's good?

These are some of the questions which increasing thousands of Catholic theologians are now asking. The old argument from the so-called "natural law" (which never convinced anyone who did not admit the magisterium of the Church and its infallibility) has not stood up, in the opinion of many theologians, under the penetrating scrutiny and examination to which it has been recently subjected.

Reflecting the thought of many Catholic scholars today, Dr. Garry Wills points out in the *National Review*: "1. It is characteristic of the human sex act not to be limited only to fertile periods and the necessities of survival but to have a spiritual function as symbolic of married union (so that 'rhythm,' by making intercourse a cyclic temporal phenomenon, returns human sexuality to the bestial level); 2. This symbolic function is a sufficient end for the sex act during infertile periods or pregnancy or after menopause; 3. There is no reason why it should not be a sufficient end when pills or contraceptives are used for the same motives that justify the practice of rhythm; 4. The only remaining objection to the use of these devices, as opposed to the scientific exploitation of infertile periods, is, in the case of the pill, a taboo about fiddling with the reproductive system (a taboo constantly violated in common medical practice) and, in the case of contraceptives, a taboo about the untamperability of the intercourse process."

While it is true that these new views have not as yet been incorporated into the official or formal teaching of the Church, they have profoundly influenced the thinking of its theologians in all countries. With 600 million members in all ranks of life and all degrees of culture, the Church must necessarily move with caution and a bit more slowly than its leading scholars. Hence Pope Paul VI affirms that "for the present" the traditional norms obtain, while he studies and mulls over the lengthy report of his commission.

Meanwhile millions of Catholics are going through the agony of trying to space their offspring in accordance with the conditions of their health and resources by the unsatisfactory rhythm method. After several heartbreaking failures, many feel compelled to form their own consciences and use more effective methods not yet approved by the Church, but which they feel will eventually be accepted. This is an agonizing decision for a Catholic, and the agony is shared by the pastoral counselor or confessor to whom the disturbed parishioner comes. This is the profoundly disturbing situation in which the Church finds itself at this writing.

In this book we have reflected the repeated pleas of hundreds of Catholic scholars in many lands, requesting a re-examination of the Church's position on birth regulation in the light of the new findings of medical science and the world's orbiting population. Along with their pleas, they presented cogent arguments for a liberalization of the present regulations without any real break in the continuity of Catholic teaching.

The modification requested would represent a *development* of doctrine, not a *contradiction*. According to traditional Catholic teaching, the morality of an act is determined by the object (the thing done), the end or purpose for which it is done, and the circumstances under which it is done. Circumstances always affect the morality of an act. For example, it is wrong to steal. But if a man is starving, he is justified in taking food. Property right yields to a human right, namely, the right to life. Thus the starving condition of the man changes completely the moral character of the act. The principle, it is wrong to steal, still remains valid. But its application is altered in this case by the starving condition of the man.

Let us apply this line of reasoning to birth regulation. When the original command, "Increase and multiply," was given by God to our first parents, Adam and Eve, the earth was uninhabited by other humans. But today large portions of it are swarming with inhabitants as in India, where millions are without proper shelter, clothing, and food, and are never free from the pangs of hunger. Hence the profound change in the circumstances or conditions of life demands a corresponding change in the application of the principle or command, "Increase and multiply."

Moreover, the findings of medical science concerning new and effective methods of regulating conception without harming the woman constitute a new and significant change in the circumstances which affect the morality of the act. While ethics is a normative science, dealing with the application of principles, it must always recognize that changes in the circumstances demand corresponding changes in the application of those principles. The latter remain valid, but the judgment concerning the morality of individual acts will vary with the concrete circumstances in each case.

Because this goes, we think, to the very heart of the hesitancy of the Church's magisterium to alter her ruling on birth regulation, let us cite another example. In the Middle Ages the Church condemned the taking of interest on money loaned as the sin of usury. But then money was normally only a medium of exchange for articles and a measure of value. Hence to charge interest on it was to attribute to money an inherently fruitful value it did not then possess.

When conditions changed and money itself became productive, the teaching of the Church changed correspondingly and a fair rate of interest was sanctioned. Here is a classic instance of a doctrinal development brought about by changed conditions. It illustrates perfectly how a similar development in the Church's teachings on birth regulation can be achieved by a frank recognition of the profound changes which have occurred since the original command was given to our first parents.

We have presented also the appeal of Nobel prize winners in the United States, Great Britain, Europe, and other countries to Pope Paul VI, urging him in making his decision to consider three crucial facts: 1. The uncontrolled growth of the world's population is a major evil of our day. 2. Unwanted children constitute a source of unhappiness, privation, and distress. 3. Parents have the right to beget only the number of children which can be properly cared for and cherished.

It is a brief but noble document, and it reflects the convictions not only of scientists and scholars but also of thoughtful men and women the world over. We are confident that it will profoundly influence the thinking of His Holiness.

What might perhaps be regarded as the climax of these appeals was the joint statement addressed to Pope Paul VI by leading theologians, churchmen, and scientists. In their well-reasoned statement, "The Moral

Imperatives for Regulating Birth," these eighty-five noted leaders express the conviction "that a new moral consensus must be achieved among leaders of all major faiths, and that man's responsibility to the next generation includes a primary duty to limit that generation's size."

Back of all these appeals is the clear consciousness that the efforts of most members of the human family to control the skyrocketing population will fail if the Catholic Church, with its 600 million members, refuses to co-operate. The human family may be likened to a group of five persons in a boat, rowing upstream against a powerful current. Each is expected to pull his share. But if one of the five—the Catholic percentage in the world's population—pulls in the opposite direction, he will largely frustrate the efforts of his fellow travelers. The appeals of all the persons cited in this book are so many pleas, courteous and earnest, to Catholics to pull their weight in the bark.

The statement issued by the twelve heads of state of Colombia, Finland, India, Malaysia, Morocco, Nepal, Republic of Korea, Singapore, Sweden, Tunisia, the United Arab Republic, and Yugoslavia on December 10, 1966, Human Rights Day, was addressed to the United Nations. But it was implicitly addressed to the magisterium of the Catholic Church as well.

"Too rapid population growth," they said, "seriously hampers efforts to raise living standards, to further education, to improve health and sanitation, to provide better housing and transportation, to forward cultural and educational opportunities, and even in some countries to secure sufficient food."

In her well-balanced and down-to-earth chapter, Clare Boothe Luce vividly depicts the unsuitableness of the complicated rhythm method for the pitifully poor and illiterate populations of the Catholic Latin-American countries. Not permitted by the Church to use the simple, cheap, and effective methods developed by medical science, millions of these women are turning in their desperation to the sad and tragic expedient of abortion.

Studies and surveys indicate that in many places in Latin America abortions are now outnumbering births. Almost audible in Mrs. Luce's chapter are the muffled cries of these agonized women for help in their distress. Their tortured cries may prove more moving than all our learned treatises and argumentation.

In our judgment virtually all the children of the Church—probably 99 per cent—will join Mrs. Luce in sharing what is generally thought to be the majority view of the papal commission: "Any physically harmless birth-control means, short of sterilization (which is sexual suicide) and abortion (which is self-violence and infanticide) should be accepted by the Church."

While the belief of the overwhelming majority of Catholics is that such a decision will eventually be reached, the concern of millions is now about the length of time needed to arrive at it. History shows how slowly the Church has moved in these matters, with cultural lags lasting at times for decades and even—in the Galileo case—for centuries. But the development of mass media of communication carrying both news and knowledge to the ends of the earth almost with the speed of light precludes such lengthy lags today. People now act, rightly or wrongly, on the basis of the information which floods the average home through radio, television, or the daily newspaper.

This is evidenced by the report made by Dr. Charles W. Westoff of Princeton University and Dr. Norman R. Ryder of Wisconsin University that a survey showed that the proportion of Catholic wives following Church doctrine by avoiding all birth-control methods or by resorting only to rhythm fell from 70 per cent in 1955 to 47 per cent in 1965. In other words, the majority of Catholic wives are now using some form of contraceptives and the percentage is constantly increasing.

The longer the papal decision is postponed, the more deeply the pain of indecision gnaws at the Catholic conscience. Then at last the tortured conscience feels it must act and does so on the basis of a physician prescribing a physically harmless, cheap, and effective means. Indeed it is widely predicted that there can be no hope even now of turning back the tide.

Such is the view expressed by the noted Catholic writer, Emmet John Hughes, in an article, "The Catholic Crisis," in *Newsweek*. "Over all," he points out, "there falls the long shadow of the birth-control dilemma. The matter distresses the life of the Church in ways almost spectacular. It frays the spirit of the faithful—as three out of four U.S. Catholics ignore Rome's clouded teaching. It thwarts the spirit of ecumenism—as nearly all other Christian churches dissent from the Catholic view. It sets the Church at odds with its own world crusade against poverty—as the three years of the papal commission's study of the issue gave men time to breed enough souls to populate 100 cities as large as Rome.

"It makes the Church's social mission most difficult precisely where its spiritual mission already seems precarious—as in a Latin America of soaring population growth. And it threatens to blur the very papal authority supposed to resolve the question. For all but the most myopic bishops now concur that a Catholic consensus already has begun to act by its own conscience, so that the papacy is left to do little more than anoint the accomplished fact."

The situation is further complicated by the widespread practice thus described by Monsignor S. J. Adamo, editor of the *Catholic Star Herald* of Camden, New Jersey: "Outstanding theologians before and after the Pope's statement [postponing his decision] have been insisting there is probable justification for a Catholic couple to use 'the pill,' at least the progesterone steroid pill. Some theologians have even gone further, including men who were *periti* or experts at Vatican Council II."

Monsignor Adamo then suggests an interesting solution: "Leave the issue open, neither approving nor disapproving [contraceptive] birth control but urging people to seek enlightenment for their own consciences . . . Isn't this what our American bishops have done in respect to the Vietnam war, a matter of life and death? . . . I don't believe this would be an abdication of moral authority but rather a humble admission that the highest authorities in the Church are no longer sincerely certain."

Joining in the world-wide plea for a change or a development in the Church's teaching on the morality of medically approved harmless methods of birth regulation are the Jesuit editors of the national weekly magazine, *America*. The editorial, "Contraception and the Synod of Bishops," attracted nationwide and even world-wide attention and brought favorable comments from medical scientists and theologians of all faiths. The editors present the views of a constantly increasing number of Catholic physicians concerning the positive and wholesome values in medically approved contraceptive methods.

The editorial begins by quoting a noted Catholic physician as follows: "In my opinion, contraception is essential for a sound Catholic family life. Yes, essential. Without reliance on contraception in certain situations, it is not possible for most couples to achieve the values proclaimed by the Church as part of the marital state. The Church will have to change her doctrine either on contraception or on marriage. It is no longer possible for the Church to maintain them both."

The editorial then observes: "These off-the-record remarks of a distinguished Catholic physician are typical of a judgment being made with increasing frequency by Catholic doctors. In the absence of a professional sampling, it would be rash to estimate how many Catholic doctors share these views. There can be no doubt, however, that the percentage is steadily increasing. Twenty-five years ago, being a 'good Catholic doctor' meant, among other things, that the physician did not prescribe contraceptive devices. Sometime recently, that particular meaning of the phrase came seriously into question.

"Many Catholic doctors still hold firmly, of course, to the papal teaching that artificial birth control is wrong (or at least that it is wrong until the Pope has made up his mind that it isn't). What is new is that there are also some—and soon there will be many—Catholic doctors who see positive as well as negative human values in the use of contraception in certain situations."

The editorial then adds: "Since doctors are engineers, by definition, when it comes to human life and health, it is impossible for many of them to see the sense of absolute 'natural law' prohibitions on particular physical techniques. So long as the technique is not harmful to anyone else and can be genuinely useful for the client's bodily and psychic health, how can nature forbid it? Contraception, as distinguished from abortion, does not kill anybody and it can provide substantial relief for couples who have serious medical reasons for temporarily or permanently avoiding a pregnancy.

"With regard to the achievement of authentically Christian family values, what greater boon could medicine give Catholic couples than the real, effective capacity to be responsible in the use of sex and its reproductive powers? How can couples give themselves to each other and to their children in the unselfish traditions of Christian love when another pregnancy in the family is a constant—and justified—worry? Physicians know as well as anyone else that pain and anxiety are part of every human life; but how can it be an irremediable part of a Christian marriage to be perennially uncertain in precisely what is most precious, the act of love and the act of life?"

The editors are careful to point out that the doctors who hold these views are not questioning the teaching authority of the Church. They recognize the responsibility of married couples to contribute to the preservation of the race. The physicians are discussing how contraception can assist parents in having responsibly sized healthy Christian families. The doctors acknowledge, of course, the right of the bishops and the Pope to speak authoritatively on the religious aspects of medicine and the family life.

What the doctors are endeavoring to do, within the framework of their profession and status in the Church, is to contribute to the theological discussion the data they are especially qualified to observe, namely, the physical and psychological impact of contraception used, not for "self-centered pleasure," but for the establishment of Christian family values. In so doing they are making a natural-law argument based on medical data. Their purpose is to assist the hierarchy in preserving the compatability and even the necessity of some use of contraception in the life of the genuinely Catholic family. The editorial then points out that the doctors are encouraged by recent developments to hope that, with sufficient financial support and official endorsement, research on reproduction will enable married couples to control fertility in ways more consonant with a sound interpersonal wedded relationship than some current contraceptive methods.

The editors are frank in saying that the financial support for such research merits top priority from Catholic universities, foundations, and the hierarchy itself. The editorial then concludes: "In view of the development of Catholic doctrine, it is obviously too early to determine whether the doctors who hold these views will prevail on the rest of the Church. In our judgment, they should. What is beyond doubt, however, is that the growth of these views within the best Catholic medical circles is symptomatic of the irrepressible ferment among Catholics in general. As the bishops meet in Rome to discuss the problems of the Church, there are few questions as urgent as those surrounding the use of contraception for the achievement of a truly Christian marriage."

The editorial appeared at the time when the Synod of Bishops was meeting in Rome to give their views to Pope Paul VI on matters of paramount importance. Surely no subject is of greater importance than that of family planning, with the population soaring at a rate unprecedented in human history. Thus did the scholarly editors of *America* render an invaluable service to the teaching authority of the Church in assisting it in solving the problem of effective family planning.

The demand of Catholics throughout the world for papal approval of some effective, harmless method of birth control came dramatically to the fore at the Third World Congress for the Lay Apostolate at Rome on October 14, 1967. Describing this development, a UPI dispatch from Rome reported that a bitter dispute over birth control rocked the Vatican-sponsored meeting. "Harsh words about the hierarchy," the dispatch said, "and demands that the laymen's views be heard added to the rebellious atmosphere. The restive laymen stole the limelight from the fifteen-day-old Synod of Bishops meeting in the Vatican to advise Pope Paul VI on Church matters."

The two meetings had been timed to coincide in the apparent assumption that the laymen would follow the bishops' guidance. Instead, the Third World Conference for the Lay Apostolate turned into a forum for the most outspoken public debate by a Catholic group meeting in Rome under Vatican sponsorship. Shouts and applause punctuated hours of heated arguments over birth control in the congress working group on family problems.

One group battled for an outspoken appeal to the Pope to lift the Church ban on artificial contraception, while others favored a mildly worded call for "responsible parenthood." Hours of angry debate ended in deadlock and the 140-member group agreed to send the motions to their co-ordinating committee without a vote.

"It would be a shame if this congress leaves without making it absolutely crystal clear that the laity is furious" over the birth control ban, Anthony Spencer, director of the London Center for Pastoral Research, told the working group.

The sentiments of the vast majority urging papal approval of medically approved effective contraceptive methods found expression in the following resolution prepared by their representatives: "The congress draws the attention of the Holy Father to the agonizing situation in which human society finds itself today, where uncontrolled population increase threatens both the good of the family and good of society.

"Many Catholic people living in the sacrament of marriage find themselves in a state of intolerable tension where, loving Christ, they believe that the practice of a variety of contraceptive techniques may be required of them and yet find that the present teaching of the Church does not accord with this belief. Facing the anguishing problem of demographic expansion, the assembly recalls the need of a clear statement by the teaching authorities of the Church, concentrated on the fundamental moral and spiritual values, without themselves proposing scientific or technical solutions, to achieve responsible parenthood, leaving the choice of means to the conscience of parents in conformity with their Christian faith and in consultation with trained medical and scientific advisers."

Much is to be said for the plan of turning this matter over to the enlightened consciences of married couples who, after conferences with their physicians, would decide what physically harmless method they would use. There is no doubt that in a comparatively short time this would lead to the solution of the problem in a manner satisfactory to all.

But even preferable to this, we believe, would be a clear unambiguous pronouncement from the Pope approving all physically harmless methods, excluding sterilization and abortion. Such a pronouncement would offer invaluable assistance to the governments now striving by might and main to cope with their orbiting populations.

Pope Paul VI has continued the great movement launched by his predecessor to increase the relevance of the Church's ministry and teachings to the needs of a rapidly changing world. His Holiness has shown understanding and sympathy with men and women of all faiths and races struggling to achieve richer and more meaningful lives. He has manifested wisdom and courage in charting new courses and in blazing new trails. His plea to the United Nations to outlaw war and establish world peace on a durable basis won him the esteem and gratitude of the world.

The whole human family now looks with hope and confidence to Pope Paul VI to announce a decision that will render it possible for the 600 million Catholics to use the findings of medical science to regulate their offspring by any harmless, medically approved, effective method. We are confident they will not be disappointed. Indeed we would like to think that within a few more years His Holiness will be again invited to address the United Nations.

This time his theme will be "Controlling the World's Exploding Population." Once again he will speak wise and inspiring words to the representatives of all nations, and give them the guidance, encouragement, and help they so desperately need to control the world's population soaring at a rate unprecedented in history. Unless we win this race, civilization and all mankind are headed for disaster and tragedy, second only to all-out nuclear warfare.